The Howard

and the Tudors

Studies in Science
and Heritage

Science and Heritage Programme

Arts & Humanities Research Council

EPSRC Engineering and Physical Sciences Research Council

University *of* Leicester

UNIVERSITY OF OXFORD

ENGLISH HERITAGE

YALE
CENTER
FOR
BRITISH
ART

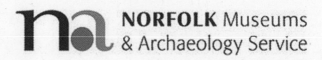
NORFOLK Museums & Archaeology Service

THE HOWARDS AND THE TUDORS

STUDIES IN SCIENCE AND HERITAGE

Edited by
PHILLIP LINDLEY

SHAUN TYAS
DONINGTON
2015

Published in 2015 by
SHAUN TYAS
1 High Street
Donington
Lincolnshire
PE11 4TA

ISBN
978-1-907730-44-3

Typeset and designed from the texts of the editor
by Shaun Tyas

IN MEMORY OF
PROFESSOR GEORGE FRASER
1955–2014

Printed and bound in the United Kingdom by
Henry Ling Ltd., at the Dorset Press, Dorchester, DT1 1HD

CONTENTS

PREFACE

The *Representing Re-Formation: Reconstructing Renaissance Monuments* collaborative project, of which this book is an important product, was awarded a major grant by the Science and Heritage programme, jointly underwritten by the Arts and Humanities Research Council and the Engineering and Physical Sciences Research Council. Our project ran between September 2010 and December 2013. We are immensely grateful to the United Kingdom Research Councils and to the whole Science and Heritage team, directed by Professor May Cassar, for their unstinting support. Baroness Sharp of Guildford, chairman of the House of Lords Science and Technology Committee, whose report in 2006 gave such a powerful impetus to conservation science, deserves the very warm thanks of everyone interested in the conservation of Britain's cultural heritage. We are also grateful to Dr Amy Meyers, Director of the Yale Center for British Art, Yale University and to the UK's JISC for additionally funding specific elements of our project.

The *Representing Re-Formation* project team was a collaborative multidisciplinary, international research group including art-historians, museologists, archaeologists, computer scientists and physicists at the University of Leicester, historians at Merton College, Oxford and at the Yale Center for British Art, Yale University, collaborating with curators, conservators, and education and imaging specialists employed by English Heritage and the Norfolk Museums and Archaeology Service.[1] The project generated a web-site, a symposium in Leicester and a two-day international conference in St Catharine's College, Cambridge, a free app, a six-month long exhibition at the Ancient House Museum in Thetford featuring laser-sintered 3D prints, an exhibition guide and an artist's video, and has spawned new projects and publications at Tewkesbury in Gloucestershire, St Edmund's, Warkton and Boughton House in Northamptonshire. Our work with Europac on 3-D laser scanning gave Europac the confidence to spin off a specialist 3D scanning company working in the arena of culture, arts and design. Enigma Interactive, who produced our Thetford app, have now developed a

[1]   The project team comprised historians: Drs Steven Gunn (Oxford) and Lisa Ford (YCBA, Yale University), with PhD student Kirsten Claiden-Yardley (Oxford); an archaeologist: Dr Jackie Hall (Leicester); art historians: Professor Phillip Lindley with PhD student Rebecca Constabel (Leicester); physicists of the Space Research Centre (Leicester): the late Professor George Fraser, Mr Piyal Samara-Ratna, with PhD student Nishad Karim; Museologists (Leicester): Drs Ross Parry and Adair Richards; Computer Scientists (Leicester): Dr Effie Law and Nicola Beddall-Hill, all collaborating with English Heritage staff, principally the curator Jan Summerfield, and the Head of Geospatial Imaging, Paul Bryan.

proof-of-concept app for Boughton House, permitting users to 'walk back' into the lost formal gardens of the late seventeenth and early eighteenth centuries. In short, the project has generated some unexpected and exciting new ideas in the sphere of heritage interpretation and conservation science.

This project's primary objective was to investigate the historical, archaeological and art-historical backgrounds of the monuments of Thomas Howard, the third of the Howard Dukes of Norfolk and his wife, and that of Henry Duke of Richmond and Somerset and his wife at Framlingham in Suffolk, and pieces associated with both monuments which had been excavated on the site of Thetford Priory (the priory is now in the care of English Heritage, as were all but two of the excavated pieces). Jan Summerfield, the English Heritage curator, was an enthusiastic supporter and participant in the project, which received the full backing of Dr Simon Thurley, then English Heritage's CEO. Additionally, we also studied the monument at Framlingham of the fourth duke's first two wives, another associated with his daughter, and the seventeenth-century retrospective monument to the earl of Surrey, executed in 1547 (son of the third duke and father to the fourth duke), as well as a large number of other excavated fragments from Thetford (unconnected with these monuments). In this work we were fully supported by the then rector, the Reverend Graham Owen, and the churchwardens Sandra Cartwright and Jeremy Schofield. Indeed, everyone at Framlingham was enormously interested in and supportive of the project.

We planned to use the physicists of the University of Leicester's Space Research Centre, led by the late Professor George Fraser, to assist us. They commissioned and processed the data derived from the 3D laser scanning of the monuments and the fragments derived from the archaeological digs. Work on the exhibition at Thetford and the accompanying app for the Priory site, both of which owed much to Dr Ross Parry, was facilitated and turned into an entirely positive and enjoyable experience by the wholehearted and enthusiastic co-operation of the director Oliver Bone and his staff from the Ancient House Museum, Thetford, and others also drawn from the Norfolk Museums and Archaeology Service.[2] The present book draws together some of the results of the project team's work on the five key monuments at Framlingham and on the excavated pieces associated with them. It is dedicated to the memory of the late George Fraser, whose sudden death deprived the project team of a warm and humorous friend as well as of a brilliant colleague.

---

[2]   The exhibition team was comprised of the following: from Leicester: Parry & Lindley; for NMAS: Oliver Bone & Melissa Hawker and conservator Sarah Norcross-Robinson; for English Heritage: Summerfield; the designer was Ian Drake.

THE HOWARD FAMILY

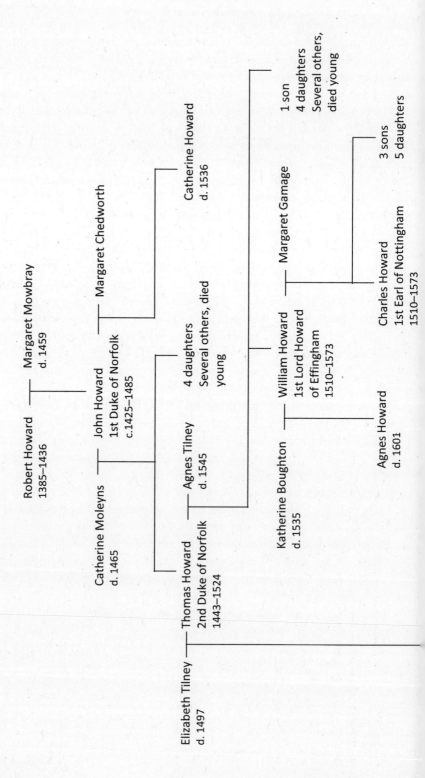

Robert Howard
1385–1436

Margaret Mowbray
d. 1459

Catherine Moleyns
d. 1465

John Howard
1st Duke of Norfolk
c.1425–1485

Margaret Chedworth

Catherine Howard
d. 1536

Elizabeth Tilney
d. 1497

Thomas Howard
2nd Duke of Norfolk
1443–1524

Agnes Tilney
d. 1545

4 daughters
Several others, died
young

Katherine Boughton
d. 1535

William Howard
1st Lord Howard
of Effingham
1510–1573

Margaret Gamage

1 son
4 daughters
Several others,
died young

Agnes Howard
d. 1601

Charles Howard
1st Earl of Nottingham
1510–1573

3 sons
5 daughters

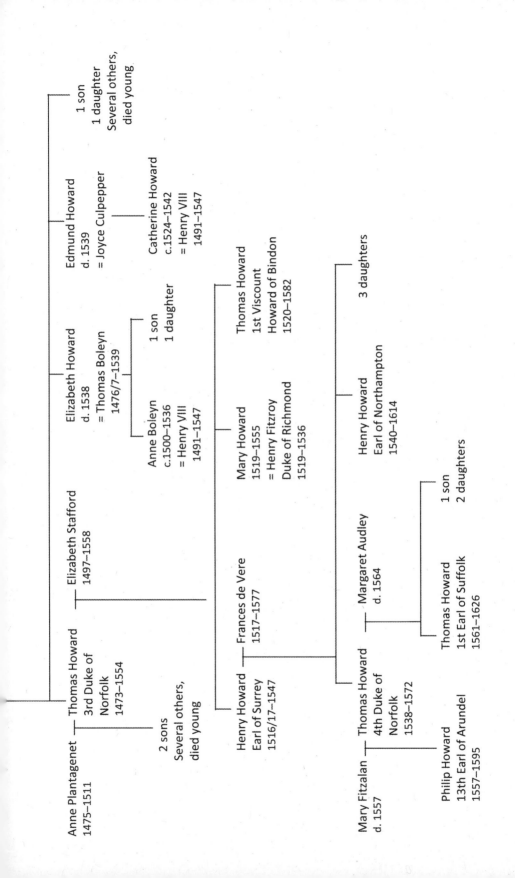

Anne Plantagenet
1475–1511
— Thomas Howard
3rd Duke of
Norfolk
1473–1554
— Elizabeth Stafford
1497–1558
Elizabeth Howard
d. 1538
= Thomas Boleyn
1476/7–1539
Edmund Howard
d. 1539
= Joyce Culpepper

1 son
1 daughter
Several others,
died young

Catherine Howard
c.1524–1542
= Henry VIII
1491–1547

2 sons
Several others,
died young

Anne Boleyn
c.1500–1536
= Henry VIII
1491–1547

1 son
1 daughter

Mary Howard
1519–1555
= Henry Fitzroy
Duke of Richmond
1519–1536

Thomas Howard
1st Viscount
Howard of Bindon
1520–1582

Henry Howard
Earl of Surrey
1516/17–1547
— Frances de Vere
1517–1577

Henry Howard
Earl of Northampton
1540–1614

3 daughters

Margaret Audley
d. 1564

Thomas Howard
1st Earl of Suffolk
1561–1626

1 son
2 daughters

Mary Fitzalan
d. 1557
— Thomas Howard
4th Duke of
Norfolk
1538–1572

Philip Howard
13th Earl of Arundel
1557–1595

INTRODUCTION

This book publishes some important results of the *Representing Re-Formation: Reconstructing Renaissance Monuments* collaborative project, funded by the Science and Heritage programme, with supplementary funding covering Dr Lisa Ford's participation, from the Yale Center for British Art, Yale University. As explained in the preface, a key objective of the collaborative project was to investigate the historical, archaeological and art-historical backgrounds of two important mid-sixteenth century monuments: that of Thomas Howard, the third Howard duke of Norfolk and of his wife; and that of Henry duke of Richmond and Somerset and his wife. Both monuments are today to be found in the chancel of St Michael's church, Framlingham in Suffolk. We also planned to scrutinise the pieces associated with both monuments which had been excavated on the site of the Cluniac church of Thetford Priory, where earlier scholars had established that the monuments now at Framlingham had originally been intended to stand. Additionally, we would also study three further monuments at Framlingham: namely, the monument of the fourth duke's first two wives; another monument generally assigned to his daughter; and the seventeenth-century retrospective monument to the earl of Surrey, executed in 1547, son of the third duke and father to the fourth duke. When I had been asked to look at the pieces of sculpture excavated at Thetford Priory, by Jan Summerfield and Dr Jackie Hall, I had discovered, or rediscovered, a large number of excavated fragments connected with the earlier Mowbray monuments at Thetford as well as some other exciting and hitherto unrecognised pieces of sculpture. It was evident from the handlist already drawn up by Dr Jackie Hall that there were also a good number of pieces of architectural sculpture and architectural components associated with the architecture of the priory church at Thetford in store, which might help her reconstruct some of the Priory Church and its architectural furniture.

What I hoped would be excitingly innovative was the plan to use the physicists of the University of Leicester's Space Research Centre, led by the late Professor George Fraser, to commission and process the data derived from the 3D laser scanning of the monuments and of the pieces discovered in the archaeological digs. We would virtually disassemble the third duke's and Richmond's monuments at Framlingham into their component pieces, and integrate, or try to integrate, the pieces which had been excavated at Thetford, to see if we could advance the work of previous art-historians, notably Dr Margaret Whinney, Professor Lawrence Stone and Sir Howard Colvin, who had pioneered the study of the monuments in the 1960s, and Professor Richard Marks, whose fundamental study in the 1980s formed the starting-point for our own work. What we aimed to do was to deploy modern scientific tools and techniques to see if we could first distinguish the different phases of work which Whinney and Marks had identified and then using 3D scanning and computer-aided design virtually deconstruct the monuments into their original components. Having achieved this, we would virtually reconstruct them as they had originally been planned, when they were intended for erection in Thetford Priory. Effectively, using 3D scanning and archaeological and art-historical analysis, we would see whether we could 're-imagine' what the third duke and his artists had intended the monuments to look like, and virtually resituate them in their originally planned locations. The third duke's plans, as will be made clear in this book, had never come to fruition, because of events alarmingly outside his control. The Dissolution of Thetford Priory had terminated work on his own and Richmond's monuments at the site; pieces of the incomplete monuments had been moved twice before they were finally set up and partially finished off forty miles away at Framlingham in Suffolk, two decades later. In the intervening years the third duke had been convicted and later exonerated of treason, his son had been executed, he had been imprisoned for several years and his lands and possessions divided up by his enemies. The duke had died a year after his release from prison and the monuments were only set up under his grandson. So, we know that the monuments we see at Framlingham today were not completed as first planned in the 1530s. What these important Tudor monuments had *originally* been intended to look like, and what range of meanings they had been intended to convey to contemporary viewers before the Dissolution of Thetford Priory in 1540 are interesting questions. Modern technology would, I hoped, enable us to test earlier scholars' ideas about the monuments and project new reconstructions of them ourselves. Simultaneously, we would investigate the Priory site at Thetford.

At the end of our project, we organised an exhibition showing off the results of our research in the Ancient House Museum, Thetford. The exhibition, which was on show from 6 September 2013 to 29 March 2014, exhibited the key components of the monuments which had been found in excavations at Thetford alongside and set into 3D scans of the monuments at 1:1 scale, 3-D scaled prints of the monuments and 2D reconstructions. The work was discussed in a substantial and copiously illustrated guidebook to the exhibition.[1] Additionally other members of the project team designed and produced an app for the Priory site.

The Physicists' work was still ongoing when the exhibition opened, and the present volume constitutes the first detailed analysis of the project, incorporating all the relevant research, from the archaeologist, art historians, historians and physicists involved. It was an immensely sad conclusion to the

---

[1]   P. Lindley, *Thetford's Lost Tudor Sculptures*, Leicester 2013.

project that Professor Fraser suddenly died whilst he was still writing his paper. In completing it, I have been only too aware that it represents his first thoughts and that there was a good deal of work which he would have rapidly drawn to a conclusion: the major developments in our scientific analysis of the monuments always came when he turned his full attention to the project and away from his challenging and important roles as Director of the Space Research centre and as Principal Investigator for the Imaging X-ray Spectrometer on ESA's Bepi-Colombo mission to the planet Mercury, scheduled for 2017. The irony that the scientific work of analysing incomplete monuments has itself been left unfinished, in spite of the work of Nishad Karim, his PhD student, would certainly not have been lost on George, who had a wonderfully sardonic sense of humour.

In this book, the historians, Dr Steven Gunn (with whom I first collaborated in the late 1980s) and his PhD student, Kirsten Claiden-Yardley, both of Merton College, Oxford, first discuss the relationships between the Tudors and the Howards from the Battle of Bosworth onwards. Their clear and concise account of a turbulent relationship provides the essential historical background. Dr Jackie Hall, the archaeologist on our team, then considers Thetford Priory, scrutinising its foundation and patronage, burials on the site, the church's architecture, the priory's Dissolution and the site's after-life. She establishes the physical context of the priory church and the long history of the Cluniac monks on the site as well as their relationships with the earls, then dukes, of Norfolk. Kirsten Claiden-Yardley next analyses noble funerals in the sixteenth century, explaining their religious and social functions and carefully discussing the changes which occurred in noble funeral ceremonies as a result of the mid-century changes in religion. My own essay focusses on the great sixteenth-century Howard monuments at Framlingham, considers their relationship to the pieces excavated on site at Thetford and suggests why the monuments look the way they do today. Kirsten next contributes a brief discussion of an important document dating to late in 1546, when a report was made on the heraldry visible within the Priory church. This is followed by an essay on the possible French connections of the Framlingham monuments by my former student, Dr Rebecca Constabel. She focuses on what monuments the third duke might have seen in France in 1533, implicitly ascribing to him a decisive role in selecting specific models for his own and son-in-law's monuments. She also contributes a remarkably innovative analysis of artists' graffito inscriptions. The late George Fraser's essay considers the scientific tools his team deployed to study the monuments and associated components and where future developments might lead. Finally, Dr Lisa Ford brings the book to a close with a fine analysis of the retrospective monument to Henry Howard earl of Surrey.

The Tudors and the Howards

STEVEN GUNN and KIRSTEN CLAIDEN-YARDLEY

The relationship between the Tudor monarchs and the Howard family did not begin well. John Howard, first duke of Norfolk of the Howard line, Lord Admiral and Earl Marshal, was killed at the battle of Bosworth in 1485 leading the vanguard of Richard III's army. His son Thomas, earl of Surrey, was badly wounded, captured on the battlefield and imprisoned by the victorious Henry VII. The Howards traced their ancestry back to Sir William, a Norfolk judge who died in 1308, but they had risen from gentility to greatness in one generation. John Howard had served the Mowbray dukes of Norfolk, one of whose daughters his father had married, and then the Yorkist kings with loyalty, skill and a steady eye to his own advancement. He gained a seat on the royal council, wide lands in East Anglia, and a place among the baronage. In 1483 he had helped put Richard III on the throne and won the dukedom of Norfolk as his reward and an earldom for his son. Now all lay in ruins, lands and titles stripped away by act of parliament in the wake of the battle.[1]

What followed was a remarkable, yet always fragile, recovery. The Howards proved themselves utterly loyal to the Tudors, reached the heights of power in successive reigns and spread their family's influence in government and society through multiple branches and overlapping generations. Yet again and again there were Howard political casualties, executions and deaths in prison. As Sir Thomas Wyatt, close friend of one of those victims, Henry Howard, earl of Surrey, noted in the refrain of one of his poems of court life, *circa regna tonat*, around the throne there is thunder.

Thomas Howard was released from the Tower of London and restored to the earldom of Surrey in 1489.[2] Tax rioters in Yorkshire had killed the earl of Northumberland and Henry VII needed a dependable governor for the North. It was an ideal opportunity for the king to test Howard's loyalty and skill. Both were amply demonstrated as he led an army to overawe the rebels and then settled down at Sheriff Hutton castle to watch the border with Scotland and supervise regional government as Henry's 'lieutenant and chief officer' north of the Trent. Through the 1490s he suppressed disorder, enforced taxation, administered justice, negotiated with the Scots and arbitrated endless quarrels

---

[1]   Anne Crawford, *Yorkist Lord: John Howard, Duke of Norfolk, c.1425–1485*, London 2010. We are grateful to Dr Kate Adcock for her helpful comments on a draft of this chapter.

[2]   For the life of the second duke, see M. J. Tucker, *The Life of Thomas Howard, Earl of Surrey and Second Duke of Norfolk, 1443–1524*, London 1964.

4

between the townsfolk of York and the clergy of the Minster. In 1496–7 came the supreme test, as James IV of Scotland invaded twice in support of the Yorkist pretender Perkin Warbeck. Each time Surrey marshalled the English defences and then struck back into Scotland as James retreated, exacting reprisals for the depredations of the Scottish army. James, a prince much given to chivalric enthusiasm, is said to have challenged the earl to single combat with Berwick-upon-Tweed as the prize, but Surrey politely declined on the grounds that Berwick was not his to give.

A truce, then a peace with the Scots followed, and Surrey was called south. A generation of Henry's senior councillors was dying off, and he needed replacements. In 1501 Surrey succeeded John, Lord Dynham as lord treasurer, head of the Exchequer. The post gave him some role in overseeing the crown's finances – though detailed policy was made by the king himself and his household officers – and a fund of patronage to distribute in the appointment of customs collectors and other officials. More generally, as a great office of state, it guaranteed him a prominent place on the king's council, which he attended assiduously, settling disputes and negotiating with foreign ambassadors. Meanwhile he drew closer to the royal family, serving as chief mourner when Henry's son Prince Arthur died in 1501, escorting Princess Margaret northwards when she sealed the Scottish peace by marrying James IV in 1503, and travelling to Flanders in 1508 to negotiate a match between Princess Mary and Charles of Habsburg, heir to the greatest European empire since Charlemagne.

As he worked his way back to power through long years of service, Thomas also steadily recovered his family's lands. Successive acts of parliament validated his claim to different parts of his father's estates and of the wider Mowbray inheritance, but he still had to buy out the titles of those to whom Henry VII had granted them. By 1500 his income from East Anglia was perhaps half what his father's had been, and Framlingham Castle, symbol of Mowbray lordship, was in his hands and undergoing repairs. By his death in 1524 he had exceeded his father's income, and when his lands in Surrey, Sussex and elsewhere were counted in, his total takings were £2,241 a year, making him probably the second richest peer in England after the earl of Northumberland. With these lands came a growing body of followers among the gentry of East Anglia and the South-East, men who raised troops to serve under him, staffed local government and sat in parliament for pocket boroughs like Horsham and Reigate.[3]

[3]   Roger Virgoe, 'The Recovery of the Howards in East Anglia, 1485–1529' in Caroline Barron et al. (eds), *East Anglian Society and the Political Community of Late Medieval England: selected papers of Roger Virgoe*, Norwich 1997, 219–34; S. T. Bindoff (ed.), *History of Parliament: The House of Commons 1509–1558* , 3 vols, London 1982, i. 196–7, 204–5.

Thomas Howard married twice and each match was prolifically fertile, especially given the high infant mortality rates of the day, to which he seems to have lost at least half a dozen children. In 1472, aged about 28, he wed Elizabeth Tilney, an East Anglian heiress who already had three children from her first marriage. In quick succession she gave him three surviving sons and two daughters, but when she died in April 1497 her lands went to her son by her first husband, John Bourchier, Lord Berners. Surrey remarried within seven months to Elizabeth's much younger first cousin, Agnes Tilney. They had three sons and four daughters.

It was a mark of Howard's political weight and disposable wealth that almost all these children made impressive marriages. His daughters matched with four earls and two viscounts, though admittedly some of these were second marriages and some of their husbands gained their peerages or promotions only after hitching themselves to the Howard political bandwagon. Where possible, his younger sons married heiresses or widows. Most remarkable were the matches contracted by his son and heir, Thomas. In 1495 Henry VII allowed him to marry Anne, daughter of Edward IV and sister of the queen, Elizabeth of York. Though they had children, none lived to adulthood, and she died in 1512. By Easter 1513 he married again, to Elizabeth, daughter of Edward Stafford, duke of Buckingham, the greatest nobleman in England, who promised a suitably lavish dowry. Three surviving children, two sons and a daughter, were born between 1517 and 1520, but in other respects the marriage was troubled. By 1526–7 Thomas had taken a long-term mistress, Elizabeth Holland, and in the 1530s his wife claimed that her husband had dragged her around the house by her hair and that his servants were instructed to tie her up and sit on her until she spat blood and her fingers bled; from 1534 they lived apart, she effectively under house arrest at his command.[4]

When Henry VII died in 1509 and was succeeded by his son Henry VIII, the elder Thomas was one of those who oversaw the smooth transition to the new reign. His second son Sir Edward Howard was especially close to the new king, a swashbuckling figure who moved easily from triumphs in the tiltyard to command of the English navy against France. In 1512 he plundered French shipping, raided the Breton coast and fought a drawn battle against a larger enemy fleet. In this action his brother-in-law Sir Thomas Knyvet was killed, and Edward reportedly vowed never to see the king until he had avenged their mutual friend. He was true to his word, for on 25 April 1513 he led a characteristically

[4] Barbara Harris, 'Marriage Sixteenth-Century Style: Elizabeth Stafford and the Third Duke of Norfolk', *Journal of Social History*, 15 (1982), 371–82. For the life of the third duke, see David M. Head, *The Ebbs and Flows of Fortune: the Life of Thomas Howard, Third Duke of Norfolk*, Athens GA 1995.

risky attack on French galleys using smaller English rowing barges, was forced overboard in hand-to-hand combat and drowned.[5]

Sir Edward had not had long to hold his grandfather's office of lord admiral, a fitting post for the family given their lasting interests in shipping and trade, but was succeeded by his elder brother, Lord Thomas, less dashing but more organised, who continued the naval war. Meanwhile a still more climactic success was at hand. In summer 1513 Henry VIII invaded France, leaving the earl and his sons behind to guard England. James IV declared war and the Howards set off to lead the defence of the North once again. On 4 September, at Alnwick, Lord Thomas, who had brought a thousand men in by sea, met his father, who had spent August mustering troops in Yorkshire. They pressed on northwards, ready to fight, Lord Thomas leading the vanguard with his brother Edmund on his right wing, the earl commanding the main body of the army, but their supplies were running low. James's army, outnumbering the English by three to two or more, occupied a formidable defensive position on Flodden Edge in the Cheviot Hills. Somehow, and soon, he had to be drawn to fight on more even terms.

On 8 September the Howards' gamble began, feinting withdrawal towards Berwick while marching to outflank the Scottish army and threaten its retreat. Early on the drizzly morning that followed they ate the last of their food and resumed their manoeuvre. By mid-afternoon James's army had moved to Branxton Hill and, goaded by cannon fire and archery, begun a disorganised assault. Edmund Howard's Lancashire and Cheshire men were driven from the field, but Lord Thomas's men from the fleet and Lord Dacre's borderers held firm and gradually the whole English army engaged the Scots in bloody close-quarter fighting. The Scots found it hard to use the fashionable continental pikes with which James had equipped them, fifteen or sixteen feet long with a single sharp point, while attacking downhill across rough country. The English wielded bills, shorter and more deadly, with one point for jabbing, another for hacking, and an axe blade for good measure. King James was killed, fighting only yards from Surrey, along with ten earls, thirteen barons and five or ten thousand of his subjects.[6]

Flodden won the Howards back the dukedom of Norfolk, conferred on the earl on 2 February 1514, when Lord Thomas was made earl of Surrey. It gained them extensive gifts of land from a grateful king. It also marked them in more emotive ways. Henry granted them an addition to their coat of arms, the visual proclamation of their ancestry and status: the red lion of the king of Scots, cut down to a demi-lion and pierced in the mouth with an arrow. About one-quarter

5   David Loades, 'Howard, Sir Edward (1476/7–1513)', *ODNB*.
6   Gervase Phillips, *The Anglo-Scots Wars, 1513–1550*, Woodbridge 1999, 111–33.

of the long epitaph placed by the second duke's tomb dealt with the Flodden campaign, which ended, as it pointedly said, with him 'honorably restored vnto his right name of duke of Norffolk'. At Norwich, two years after the battle, a Lancashire priest got into deep trouble for defacing a copy of a pamphlet recounting the Howards' victory and claiming that while Edmund Howard had fled the field, the Lancashire men had fought 'right valiantly'. Thirty years later, Henry Howard, the victor's grandson, scorned in verse a lady who had refused him a dance:

> How can you thus entreat a lion of that race
> That with his paws a crowned king devoured in the place?[7]

The new duke resumed his duties as councillor and diplomat, escorting the king's sister Princess Mary to her wedding with Louis XII of France – her engagement to Charles of Habsburg having been broken off – in 1514. But as he aged, it was increasingly his son, the new earl of Surrey, who was busy in royal service. In 1517 he took charge of pacifying the Evil May Day riots by disgruntled and xenophobic London apprentices, and in December 1522 he took over from his father as lord treasurer. When the old duke died in 1524, he was ready to take his place at the head of the family. Yet the political world he faced was different from that in which his father had rebuilt the family fortunes.

Henry VIII was readier than his father had been to promote his favourite courtiers to power and wealth, and in Charles Brandon, duke of Suffolk, he had created an uncomfortable neighbour for the Howards. They were outraged at his presumptuous marriage to the king's sister – the widowed Mary, queen of France – in 1515. They resented his taking the office of Earl Marshal, national arbiter in matters of honour and chivalry and patron of the heralds, at the death of the second duke, who had held it since 1510; the Howards wrestled it back in 1533. Their local followers clashed with his from time to time and it must have been a relief when the king moved Suffolk's landed base to Lincolnshire after the revolts of 1536.[8] More worrying still, Henry put faith in mighty ministers who took a stronger grip on the formation and execution of royal policy than their colleagues on the council thought was healthy. First came Thomas Wolsey, lord chancellor and cardinal from 1515 and then Thomas Cromwell, king's secretary, lord privy seal and vice-gerent in spirituals, the king's right-hand man as he took control of the English church in the 1530s.

[7] John Weever, *Ancient funerall monuments*, London 1631, 837–9; Steven Gunn, David Grummitt, Hans Cools, *War, State and Society in England and the Netherlands, 1477–1559*, Oxford 2007, 208–9, 219–20; W. A. Sessions, *Henry Howard, the Poet Earl of Surrey: a Life*, Oxford 1999, 225.
[8] S. J. Gunn, *Charles Brandon, duke of Suffolk, c.1484–1545*, Oxford 1988, 36–7, 78–82, 121–7, 165–74.

Historians debate how actively Norfolk opposed Wolsey and Cromwell, how successfully he and others at court plotted against them and convinced the king, at length, to destroy each of them and re-invent himself as a monarch taking the counsel of his natural advisers, the great nobility. It is always tempting to read politics backwards from the eventual outcome, plotting by its nature leaves thin traces, and we cannot get inside Henry VIII's head to see how far he was the puppet-master of court politics, how far the plaything of faction. The third duke certainly worked with Wolsey and Cromwell to serve the king; he had to. But foreign ambassadors and other observers thought he resented their dominance and acted to undermine it. The Spanish ambassador wrote in 1529 of an alliance between Norfolk, Suffolk and Anne Boleyn 'to overthrow the cardinal'; the French ambassador in 1540 of how the duke of Norfolk and others were 'open enemies' of Cromwell and his friends, the two groups 'trying to destroy each other'.[9]

Certainly Norfolk fell foul of the ministers' efforts to impose the king's authority conspicuously on his most powerful subjects. In 1516 he was temporarily excluded from the council for breaking the laws on retaining liveried followers. In 1525 he lost the lord admiralship so it could be given to the king's illegitimate son. Under Cromwell he repeatedly complained that he was kept away from court. Certainly too he benefited from their downfalls. When Wolsey fell from power in 1529 over his failure to secure the king's divorce from Katherine of Aragon, Norfolk moved to the forefront among the king's advisers. As the Venetian ambassador reported in November 1530, 'His Majesty uses him in all negotiations more than any other person.'[10] The same happened again in 1540 when Cromwell, discredited by the king's disastrous marriage with Anne of Cleves, was destroyed on charges that he had promoted heresy within the church. On the day after Cromwell's execution, the French ambassador wrote that Norfolk now had the chief role in managing the king's affairs. Yet Norfolk never managed to establish his own dominance in the king's counsels for long. Perhaps, a natural team player, he did not wish to. More likely he had too little finesse, too little administrative grasp, too many enemies.

---

[9] David Starkey, *The Reign of Henry VIII: Personalities and Politics*, London 1985, 81–101, 121–33; Peter Gwyn, *The King's Cardinal: the Rise and Fall of Thomas Wolsey*, London 1990, 565–70; E. W. Ives, 'The Fall of Wolsey', in S. J. Gunn and P. G. Lindley (eds), *Cardinal Wolsey: Church, State and Art* (Cambridge 1991), 286–315; Steven Gunn, 'The Structures of Politics in early Tudor England', *Transactions of the Royal Historical Society*, 6th series 5 (1995), 59–90; G. W. Bernard, 'The Fall of Wolsey Reconsidered', *Journal of British Studies*, 35 (1996), 277–310; J. S. Brewer et al (eds), *Letters and Papers, Foreign and Domestic, of the Reign of Henry VIII*, 23 vols. in 38, London, 1862–1932, iv (iii). 5255, xv. 767.

[10] Head, *Ebbs and Flows of Fortune*, 103.

The third duke, like his father, undertook occasional embassies, notably to France in 1533 and 1540; but the opportunities to serve the king in which he felt most at home came in warfare. As he spluttered in 1536, he was not one to 'sit still lyk a man of law' when there was fighting to be done.[11] In 1520–1 he was lord lieutenant of Ireland, where he tried to settle disputes among the Anglo-Irish magnates, improve the lordship's finances and raid vigorously against the Gaelic lords, but never had enough money or men for more thoroughgoing conquest.[12] In 1522, as Henry reopened war with France, he led a successful naval raid on Morlaix in Brittany and a more frustrating foray into Picardy in co-operation with Habsburg captains, which produced nothing but a failed siege of Hesdin. In 1523–4 he alternated devastating raids into Scotland and resistance to Scottish incursions with attempts to install a pro-English regime around James V.

Campaigning resumed in the 1540s. In October 1542 Norfolk led a large but under-supplied invasion of Scotland which achieved little more than the sacking of Kelso. In 1544, in Henry's last great effort to emulate the heroic kings of the Hundred Years War, he was sent to besiege Montreuil as a distraction to the French while the king battered Boulogne into submission. Efforts at Montreuil were hamstrung by bickering with the Habsburgs' generals, thin provisions and inadequate tactics, but it scarcely mattered since Henry won his prize. Norfolk and his colleagues had more explaining to do in October, when they retreated to Calais and thus risked losing Boulogne back to the French, but the fortress survived. Next year, as the French threatened invasion, he was still trusted enough to be put in charge of the defences of East Anglia. All these ventures made use of and reinforced the Howards' ties to their servants, tenants and gentry followers in Norfolk, Suffolk and Sussex as they called on them to fight in their retinues, raise troops and lead companies under their command. Shared perils and shared glory bound them closely to such men. Henry Howard recalled his brotherhood in arms with Thomas Clere:

> Aye me, while life did last that league was tender
> Tracing whose steps thou sawest Kelsal blaze,
> Landrecy burnt, and battered Boulogne render.[13]

In 1525, 1528 and 1536 Norfolk mobilised against domestic rebels. The Amicable Grant troubles of 1525 were merely vociferous tax protests; he combined with the duke of Suffolk to confront the rebels in Suffolk and order them home while conveying their grievances to the king, who cancelled his demands for excessive and unparliamentary taxation. In 1528 there was unrest

---

11 Head, *Ebbs and Flows of Fortune*, 136.
12 Steven G. Ellis, *Ireland in the Age of the Tudors 1447–1603*, London 1998, 119–26.
13 Gunn, Grummitt and Cools, *War, State and Society*, 140–2, 200–1, 208; Sessions, *Henry Howard*, 303.

in Norfolk over high food prices and the suspension of cloth exports, but again it was readily contained by swift action. The Pilgrimage of Grace of 1536–7 was a much more serious matter, prompted by opposition to the dissolution of the monasteries and Henry's other changes in the church, but complicated by fears about taxation, the royal succession, southern domination of the North and oppression of tenants by their landlords. Norfolk led a hopelessly outnumbered royal army to face the rebels across the River Don and negotiated a truce on 27 October 1536. As autumn turned to winter he kept the rebel leaders talking, at length offering a royal pardon for all and a session of Parliament at York to consider their grievances, the only terms on which he could get them to disperse. While he traded on the northerners' confidence in him as the veteran of Flodden, he had already assured Henry that he would not consider himself bound by any 'oath nor promise made for policy to serve you mine only master and sovereign'.[14] Renewed trouble in January and February gave Henry the excuse to send him back to execute leading rebels and preside over renewed monastic dissolutions.

Military service would also prove a consistent means for junior members of the dynasty to win promotion. Edmund Howard, third son of the second duke by his first wife, worsted at Flodden, was ineffectual even in the lacklustre posting of comptroller of Calais, a job he was given in 1531 to help him repair his debt-ridden finances. But others did better. William Howard, eldest son of the second duke by his second wife, set out on a diplomatic career, with several embassies to Scotland and France in the 1530s. But it was the wars of the 1540s that took him to the top. In 1552–3 he commanded England's last remaining continental outpost as lord deputy of Calais and in 1554 he became lord admiral and Baron Howard of Effingham. He served Elizabeth loyally as councillor and courtier and bequeathed his title in 1573 to his son Charles, who would command the English fleet against the Spanish Armada.[15] Thomas Howard, second son of the third duke, was soundly endowed by his marriage to his father's ward, Elizabeth Marney, co-heiress to her father John, Lord Marney. He was knighted for his role at the crushing English victory over the Scots at Pinkie in 1547. In 1559, at Elizabeth's coronation, he was created Viscount Howard of Bindon, planting another Howard line in the peerage.[16] Charles Howard, Queen Catherine's brother, slipped away from her downfall to fight against the Turks and returned to be knighted when the English burnt Edinburgh

[14] M. E. James, 'English Politics and the Concept of Honour, 1485–1642', in his *Society, Politics and Culture: Studies in Early Modern England*, Cambridge 1986, 341–2.

[15] James McDermott, 'Howard, William, first Baron Howard of Effingham (c.1510–1573)', *ODNB*.

[16] *Complete Peerage*, vi. 583–4.

in 1544.[17] His brother George carried the English standard at Pinkie and went on to serve Elizabeth for twenty years as master of the armoury.[18]

Court politics and royal marriages offered more glittering prizes than warfare, but proved considerably more deadly. For the Howards there were both opportunities and dangers in the fact that Henry's choice of queen to replace Katherine of Aragon was the third duke's niece Anne Boleyn. The tense politics of the break with Rome and the king's divorce destroyed one Howard son-in-law early on, Rhys ap Gruffydd, husband of the second duke's daughter Catherine. With the vigorous support of his wife, he had thrown his weight about in the politics of South Wales for years. This assertiveness lent credence to accusations in autumn 1531 that, inspired by ancient Welsh prophecies, he had plotted with James V of Scots to depose Henry and make himself prince of Wales. Trial and execution followed swiftly.[19]

Kinship with Anne Boleyn's daughter Elizabeth gave the Howards prominence at court in the short run – the princess's godmother, for example, was the dowager duchess – and a call on Elizabeth's favour when, at length, she became queen. But Anne was a vigorous politician in her own right and her relations with the duke were stormy. Her rise did not profit him as much as he had doubtless hoped, but her fall in 1536 in a bloody maelstrom of court intrigue and royal suspicion did little for him either. It was probably through Anne's influence that the duke's daughter Mary also married into the royal family. On 26 November 1533 she wed Henry Fitzroy, the king's bastard son whom he had recognised and created duke of Richmond in 1525. Fitzroy became fast friends with his brother-in-law Henry Howard and might yet have featured in King Henry's succession plans, but on 23 July 1536 he succumbed to illness, leaving his widow to two decades of piety, poetry and survival on the perilous fringe of the court.[20]

In 1536–7 another Howard was destroyed by the labyrinthine politics of marriage and succession around Henry VIII. Thomas Howard, second son of the second duke by his second wife, was a poet and courtier. In 1535 he fell in love with Lady Margaret Douglas. She was, reported the French ambassador, 'beautiful and highly esteemed', but she was also dangerously closely related to the royal family at a time when Henry VIII still had no son and there were questions over the legitimacy of both his daughters. Her father was the earl of Angus, but her mother was the dowager queen of Scots, Margaret, daughter of Henry VII. In due course this Tudor blood would make her son, Henry Lord

[17] Lacey Baldwin Smith, *A Tudor Tragedy: The Life and Times of Catherine Howard*, London 1961, 200; W. A. Shaw, *The Knights of England*, 2 vols, London 1906, ii, 55.
[18] Bindoff, *Commons*, ii. 399–401.
[19] Ralph A. Griffiths, *Sir Rhys ap Thomas and his Family: a Study in the Wars of the Roses and Early Tudor Politics*, Cardiff 1993, 88–111.

Darnley, an attractive if disastrous match for Mary Queen of Scots. For the moment it just spelt danger for Thomas Howard. His secret engagement to marry Lady Margaret was discovered in July 1536, both were put in the Tower and he was condemned to death by act of parliament for imperilling the succession by marrying her without the king's permission. The sentence was not carried out, but he died in prison in October 1537. She lived on to fall for another Howard in 1541, Queen Catherine's brother Charles, another romance proscribed by the king.[21]

King Henry's troubled love life lured more Howards to destruction in 1542.[22] Part of Norfolk's role in the undoing of Thomas Cromwell had been the provision of his teenaged niece Catherine Howard, daughter of his younger brother Lord Edmund, as a tempting replacement for Anne of Cleves. She married the king on the day Cromwell was executed, 28 July 1540, and jobs and flavours began to flow satisfyingly to her Howard kin. In November 1541, however, devastating revelations emerged. Not only had the queen been intimate with young men while living in her grandmother's household before her marriage, one of them having, as she confessed, 'used me in such sort as a man doth his wife many and sundry times'. Worse, she had entertained nocturnal visits from a gentleman of the court during the summer's royal progress. Condemned in parliament, she was beheaded on 13 February 1542. Her fall threatened her wider family, tried for concealing her offences, sentenced to lose all their goods and imprisoned. Her uncle William, the future Lord Howard of Effingham, was incarcerated for nearly a year, the dowager duchess in whose house her indiscretions had begun for six months, William's wife and Catherine's aunt the countess of Bridgewater more temporarily. Norfolk rapidly disassociated himself from them all with a grovelling letter to the king.

It was harder for Norfolk to disown the waywardness of his son and heir, Henry Howard, earl of Surrey.[23] Surrey grew up with a fiery pride in his noble line and an eloquent gift for verse. Sadly his control of metre and rhyme was not matched by mastery of his passions. 'We shall have a maddening time in our youth' was his excuse when, at the age of 26, a riotous night in London and Southwark, breaking the townsfolk's windows with stones shot from crossbows and harassing apprentices and whores, got him and his friends locked up in the Fleet prison in March 1543. Happy marriage to Frances de Vere, daughter of the earl of Oxford, and fatherhood, with two sons and three daughters born between 1536 and 1547, matured him, but not enough. He ached to prove himself in battle as his forebears had done. When put in charge at Boulogne in 1545–6 he

20 Beverley A. Murphy, *Bastard Prince: Henry VIII's Lost Son*, Stroud 2001, 123–5, 143–5, 174–7, 219–41.
21 Michael Riordan, 'Howard, Lord Thomas (c.1512–1537)', *ODNB*; Rosalind K. Marshall, 'Douglas, Lady Margaret, countess of Lennox (1515–1578)', *ODNB*.

did well at maintaining the beleaguered town's lines of supply, extending its fortifications and keeping the French at arm's length, but got little thanks from his father and his fellow councillors, who wished the king would rest on his laurels and make peace. On 7 January 1546 he led thousands of men to ambush a heavily-guarded French supply column near St Etienne. Ninety French wagons were destroyed, but Surrey's pikemen fled, leaving their captains to be killed or captured. The earl was swept back with his men, shouting at them to turn and fight, allegedly calling in despair for his companions to run him through in the midst of his dishonour. Within weeks he knew he would be removed from command and on 27 March he was back at court.

Through the spring, summer and autumn of 1546 political tension wound tighter and tighter. The king was old and ill and Prince Edward still young. Someone – Surrey repeatedly told his friends it should be Norfolk – would have to govern the realm as protector if anything happened to Henry. Disputes over religion racked the court, resulting most obviously in the burning of Anne Askew, a gentlewoman with friends in very high places, in July. Surrey's taste for translating Scripture into English and breaking the Lenten fast gave him links to those who wanted to take England further towards continental Protestantism, but his father stood for religious conservatism. Norfolk was happy enough to take the lands of dissolved monasteries to strengthen his East Anglian landholdings: Bungay, Butley, Castle Acre, Coxford, Sibton, Thetford. But he had no truck with new-fangled teachings. 'It was mery in Yngland affore the new lernyng came up', he was reported to have said, he 'nev[er] rede [th]e scripture nor nev[er] wolde rede it', and he wished 'all thyng[es] were as it hathe beyne in tymez paste'.[24] The duke might play a long game, but Surrey was too mercurial for that, too ready to complain about the men of low birth promoted by the king and the way they were ruining the realm. Already in 1543 there had been rash talk among servants of the London houses he frequented that he was a prince, and one who might be king if anything untoward happened to Henry and his son. Now evidence emerged that Surrey did indeed aspire to the throne. On 2 December he was arrested for questioning, ten days later marched to the Tower, where his father joined him.

Though there was talk of planned coups and betrayal of state secrets and attempts to install the duchess of Richmond as a royal mistress, the primary charges, angrily annotated by the fading king, concerned the heraldry used by Norfolk and, in particular, Surrey. Making free with the arms of St Edward the Confessor, Geoffrey Plantagenet, count of Anjou and Thomas of Brotherton, brother of Edward II and earl of Norfolk, it was alleged, suggested kingly ambitions. The evidence of what had been done and whether the Howards had

[22] Smith, *A Tudor Tragedy*.

the right to do it was murky at best, but it was enough.[25] Surrey was rapidly tried and convicted, railing against the 'conjured league' of those who had accused him, turncoat Howard followers combining with the rival courtiers, mostly of reforming religious inclinations, who now stood to take power when the king breathed his last. Doubtless those rivals put pressure on the king to neutralise the Howards before it was too late; doubtless the king thought he was still in control, dictating the future from the edge of the grave. Certainly Norfolk saw himself as the victim of one last and fatal plot. In the course of his career he had had so many 'great enemies', he reflected self-pityingly from the Tower, that it was only because he had been 'a most true man to my sovereign lord', that he had survived, for 'there was never gold tried better by fire and water than I have been'. Not only had Wolsey and Cromwell 'gone about ... to have destroyed me', but Brandon and others had urged Wolsey on, and he had endured the hatred of his father-in-law Buckingham, his son-in-law Rhys ap Gruffydd, and last but not least 'both my nieces, that it pleased the king's highness to marry'.[26] Now there was no escape, or so it seemed.

At the Howards' arrest the king's men moved quickly to confiscate their goods and houses. The inventories they produced are the best guide we have to the wealth and sophistication of the family's life.[27] They maintained three great houses in East Anglia in addition to Lambeth in Surrey. Framlingham Castle in Suffolk had been refurbished by the second duke with new lodgings, big windows and fashionable carved brick chimneys. Kenninghall in Norfolk was built by the third duke in the 1520s, a brick palace to rival Wolsey's Hampton Court or Charles Brandon's Westhorpe. It had suites of rooms for the duke, Surrey, his wife, his sister, his younger brother Thomas and the duke's mistress Bess Holland. It had a long gallery with 28 portraits of 'divers noble persons', a great chamber with fourteen tapestries depicting Hercules, an indoor tennis court and a chapel with two organs, a gilt wooden altarpiece 12 feet by 5, six tapestries of the Passion, each 9 square yards in size, and 42 copes for the choir. Surrey drove himself into debt building something more startling still, Mount Surrey, just outside Norwich. Quite how classicising it was in style is now hard to say – part of a stone mantelpiece carved with acanthus leaves survives – but it was

23 For Surrey's life, see Sessions, *Henry Howard*.
24 TNA, SP1/163, fo. 38r.
25 Peter R. Moore, 'The Heraldic Charge Against the Earl of Surrey, 1546–47', *English Historical Review*, 116 (2001), 557–83.
26 N. Pocock (ed.), Gilbert Burnet, *The History of the Reformation of the Church of England*, 7 vols, Oxford 1865, vi. 276–7.
27 TNA, LR2/115–117. For an inventory of Framlingham in 1524, see J. M. Ridgard (ed.), *Medieval Framlingham: Select Documents 1270–1524*, Suffolk Records Society 27, Woodbridge 1985, 129–58.

large and its interiors were assertive. There were huge tapestries and Turkish carpets. The earl had a chair of estate upholstered in purple velvet and satin, embroidered with silver and gold lace and adorned with silver knobs. Lest one forget his martial ambitions, he had two gilt rapiers engraved with antique – classical – designs.[28]

Surrey had learned his taste for renaissance style at the French court, where he stayed with Henry Fitzroy in 1532–3, drinking in the Italianate decoration of Fontainebleau and encountering the latest in French and Italian poetry. All this influenced not only his house, but also his poetic experimentation, leading to the invention of the English blank verse that Spenser and Shakespeare would take to new heights. His elders had not been poets, but they were not devoid of learning or literary interests. His grandfather may well have written a memoir of the politics of his early life in the style of contemporary Burgundian and French courtiers.[29] His father liked to drop Latin phrases into his letters and asked in the Tower to be sent Augustine's *City of God* for some improving reading. In each generation the Howards patronised leading writers and intellectuals. The second duke favoured the poets Alexander Barclay, who wrote an elegy for Sir Edward, and John Skelton, who stayed with his family at Sheriff Hutton in the 1490s. The third duke consulted, supported or employed fashionable humanist scholars such as John Leland the antiquarian, Roger Ascham the educationalist and Hadrianus Junius, a Dutch physician. After Surrey's death the duchess of Richmond employed John Foxe, the future author of the Book of Martyrs, as tutor to his children.

Surrey was beheaded on 19 January 1547. His father, condemned by parliament, was to have followed him, but Henry himself died in the night of 27–28 January and execution was stayed. For six and a half years Norfolk sat in the Tower, permitted a servant, occasional family visits, and freedom to walk in the gardens and grounds. Then, miraculously, Edward died, his nominated successor Lady Jane Grey faltered, and Mary took the throne. Released, pardoned and restored, Norfolk took his place as Earl Marshal at Mary's coronation and sat regularly in her council. In January 1554 she called him out for his last military campaign, against the revolt raised in Kent by Sir Thomas Wyatt in protest at her plans to marry Philip of Spain. At Rochester some of his London companies defected en masse to Wyatt and he had to retreat, leaving the defeat of the rebels to younger men. That summer East Anglia welcomed

---

[28] Sessions, *Henry Howard*, 143–9, 168–74, 217–20; Maurice Howard, *The Early Tudor Country House: Architecture and Politics 1490–1550*, London 1987, 114–16.

[29] D. A. L. Morgan, 'Hearne's "Fragment" and the Long Prehistory of English Memoirs', *English Historical Review*, 124 (2009), 811–32.

him home to settle his affairs: he made his will at Kenninghall on 21 July and died there on 25 August.

His grandson and heir Thomas Howard, born in 1538, was already preparing to perpetuate the family's greatness.[30] One task facing him was to regain control of the family lands, many of which had been sold or given away by the crown since 1547. By his death the third duke had succeeded in recovering perhaps two-thirds of the lands he had had in his prime, making a fine inheritance worth some £2,500 a year. But years of negotiation and sales of standing timber to raise cash lay ahead to extend the estate, concentrate it further on East Anglia and clear various debts to the crown. Another duty was to perpetuate the dynasty. Thomas married the scholarly Mary Fitzalan, daughter of the earl of Arundel, in 1555. In June 1557 she bore a son, named Philip for his godfather the king, but she never recovered from the birth, dying two months later. In November 1558 he married again, to Margaret, daughter and heir of Thomas Lord Audley, already a widow herself at 18. She would bear him two sons and two daughters before she too died, again in the aftermath of childbirth, in 1564.

Mary's reign had offered him no great opportunities, but the accession of her sister Elizabeth called him to the fore. At first duty was straightforward and pleasurable, serving as Earl Marshal at the coronation and a challenger at the coronation tournament, welcoming ambassadors to court. Matters soon became more complicated as Norfolk was drawn deep into high politics by his concerns about the queen's relationship with Lord Robert Dudley. Relations between him and the favourite deteriorated fast and it may have been in part to separate them that the duke was posted North in December 1559. His delicate task was to oversee English intervention in the crisis then developing in Scotland, aiding the Protestant lords to overthrow the French regime headed by Mary of Guise, mother of Mary, queen of Scots, without reawakening fears of English conquest. Though the incompetence of his subordinates brought setbacks on campaign, he maintained sufficient pressure on the French and their allies to bring on the Treaty of Edinburgh in July 1560, by which French and English troops alike withdrew, leaving the Lords of the Covenant to run Scotland. Next year his and Dudley's followers were bickering in London and in October 1562 they joined the privy council neck and neck as the queen lay ill with smallpox. Consistently the duke backed plans for Elizabeth to marry not Dudley, but the Archduke Charles of Habsburg. Repeatedly he fell out with Dudley, from 1564 earl of Leicester; in early 1566 it came to the pass of Leicester's friends wearing blue at court and Norfolk's allies yellow.

[30] For the fourth duke's life, see Neville Williams, *Thomas Howard, Fourth Duke of Norfolk,* London 1964.

Power in East Anglia was easier to exercise than power at court. The duke readily took up his ancestors' leading role in the politics of Norfolk, where his gentlemen followers and allies dominated local government and he served as lord lieutenant, in command of the county militia.[31] He refurnished Kenninghall, adding new paintings and hangings and yet more Turkish carpets. At Norwich he greatly enlarged his grandfather's townhouse, making a palatial residence with a bowling alley, a tennis court and a playhouse as well as still more sumptuous tapestries and presses full of Latin and Italian books.[32] At both he offered lavish hospitality. He looked to the interests of local towns, encouraging the repair of Great Yarmouth harbour and the renewal of Norwich's cloth industry by Flemish Protestant immigrants. In return King's Lynn, Norwich and Yarmouth regularly let him nominate at least one of their MPs.

Yet Norfolk's ambitions stretched well beyond his native county. As Earl Marshal he revelled in his direction of the heralds and jurisdiction over matters of honour. In 1565 he bought the Charterhouse, the grandest private residence in London, and enlarged it further. In 1567 he married again, to the widowed Elizabeth, Lady Dacre, planning a marriage between her children with their wide estates in the far North-West and his own. She died within months but he pressed ahead, all the more profitably after a further tragedy when little George Lord Dacre, aged 8, was killed by the collapse of his wooden vaulting-horse at the duke's house in Thetford in May 1569; now his sisters, contracted to Norfolk's sons, would inherit all the Dacre lands. Norfolk's ambition reached higher still. In 1568 he listened with interest when councillors of Mary, queen of Scots, now a deposed exile in England, suggested he might marry her. Thus Mary might be safely restored to the Scottish throne and Norfolk might do his noble best for the stability of England by resolving the thorny question of who might succeed Elizabeth if the queen continued to refuse to marry and bear heirs.

The plan rapidly became entangled with politics too deep for Norfolk to navigate, with plots by Mary's supporters, by English courtiers opposed to William Cecil's supremacy among Elizabeth's advisers, and by northern peers anxious to reverse the Reformation and their own marginalisation in regional government. When Elizabeth learnt what was afoot and summoned Norfolk to explain, he withdrew in perplexity to Kenninghall, claiming to be ill and protesting he would not have acted without the queen's approval. It was not enough. He spent eight months in the Tower, then thirteen more or less confined

[31] A. Hassell Smith, *County and Court: Government and Politics in Norfolk 1558–1603*, Oxford 1974, 21–44.
[32] Again it is the surveys and inventories taken after his fall that provide the best evidence: Williams, *Thomas Howard*, 43–6, 68–70; TNA, E164/46, LR1/43, SP12/81, fos 67–82.

to the Charterhouse, all the while sending letters of submission to Elizabeth and coded pledges of devotion to Mary. Reluctantly but fatally he was sucked into further plots managed by Roberto Ridolfi, a Florentine banker he had met through his complex financial affairs. These involved a Spanish invasion with papal backing to put Mary and Norfolk on the English throne, treason without a doubt and an odd course for a man who protested to the end his loyalty to Protestantism; events seem to have been running way with the duke. The interception of ciphered letters and bags of gold and interrogations of Norfolk and his servants provided the evidence needed for a trial. In January 1572 he was convicted, but Elizabeth hesitated to execute him until pressured by members of parliament anxious for her safety. He was beheaded on 2 June.

The fourth duke's fall was followed by that of his son, Philip, earl of Arundel, who had inherited the lands and title of his Fitzalan grandfather. Taking no heed of his father's advice to 'beware of blind papistry', he tried to flee Elizabethan England as a Catholic dissident in 1585 and spent his last nine years in the Tower. Yet the Howards endured to prosper again, managing to take to heart the fourth duke's other advice to his children, to 'beware of the court, except it be to do your prince service'. Charles, Lord Howard of Effingham won the earldom of Nottingham from the parsimonious Elizabeth for his success in naval command. Elizabeth's successor James VI and I made the poet earl's son Henry Howard, a scholarly man of Catholic leanings, earl of Northampton and one of his leading councillors. The fourth duke's younger son Thomas Howard, Elizabethan naval hero turned corrupt lord treasurer and builder of Audley End, he promoted to the earldom of Suffolk. Charles I made another cadet line Lords Howards of Escrick. The Howards' remarkable resilience had not passed with the Tudor era and the dukes of Norfolk, their title restored in 1660, remain England's premier peers to this day.

Thetford Priory:
Patronage, Burial, Buildings, Dissolution

JACKIE HALL

The Foundation

Thetford Priory was founded by Roger Bigod, a close ally of William the Conqueror, in 1103 or 1104 in the reign of Henry I. This was instead of a pilgrimage to the Holy Land that he had vowed to make. He chose the order of Cluny for his foundation and twelve monks were sent from Lewes Priory in Sussex, the oldest foundation in England. His charter includes the standard terms about the foundation being for the benefit of his soul and that of his wife (and the king and his wife), and also explicitly leaves their bodies, and the bodies of all his freemen, for burial within the bounds of the priory.[1]

Initially occupying a site on the Suffolk side of the river, previously and briefly the location of the East Anglian cathedral and later the site of the Dominican friary (now the grammar school), within a few years the Cluniacs moved to a more spacious site on the Norfolk side, where the ruins can be found today (Fig. 1). The priory was generously endowed at its foundation, and received many further gifts through the centuries, making it moderately wealthy; in 1535 it was in the top 20% of religious houses as ranked by wealth.[2] Like all Cluniac houses, it was subject to the mother house of Cluny in France and from the thirteenth century Cluniac priors were meant to attend an annual meeting there. It was also subject to 'visitation' by other Cluniac priors, to make sure that religious life was properly kept. In Cluniac houses, there was great emphasis on lengthy and ornate church services and, by comparison with Cistercian houses, no discouragement to equally ornate decoration.

As in most monasteries, life at Thetford Priory was reasonably uneventful with some notable exceptions including, for instance, the murder of its prior in 1248, occasional acts of immorality and periods of indebtedness.[3] The latter was particularly acute in the fourteenth century, when the crown was repeatedly exacting taxes or 'loans' to pay for foreign wars. Cluniac houses were in a

1 Thomas Martin,*The History of the Town of Thetford, in the Counties of Norfolk and Suffolk, from the Earliest Accounts to the Present Time,* London 1779, 116.
2 D. Dymond (ed.), *The Register of Thetford Priory,* 2 vols, Norfolk Record Society, 59 & 60 (1995–6), 1.
3 W. Page (ed.),*Victoria County History of Norfolk,* London 1906, vol. 2, 363–9; G. Charvin (ed.), 1*Statuts, Chapitres Generaux et Visites de l'Ordre de Cluny,* Paris 1965–70, 6 vols.

delicate position because of the allegiance they owed to a French house, and most of them eventually naturalised; Thetford was 'made denizen' in 1376.

Throughout, the relationship between the priory and its founders remained important. Foundation was not a one-off transaction, since the patronage of a religious house passed to the heirs of the original founder, just like property or titles. The patron was usually known as the 'founder' even generations after the original foundation. At Thetford, the relationship was unusually close (see burials, below) with the Bigods taking an interest in their East Anglian properties (barring various periods when they were confiscated by the king) until the end of that line in 1306. Patronage then passed to Thomas of Brotherton (in 1312), then his daughter, followed by the Mowbrays (1397), and then the Howard family (1483). Like the Bigods, the last two Mowbray dukes and all the Howard dukes (up to the Dissolution) made Thetford Priory their burial place and locus of familial piety.

Staying at the Priory
For the patrons, the priory was not just used as a repository of prayer and burial, important though that was, it was also used as a meeting place and a place to stay, being a good day's journey (35 miles) from the chief residence of the earls and dukes of Norfolk at Framlingham Castle and 13 miles from Kenninghall, the house used by the later Howards. We can see this most clearly in the time of the Howards, from the late medieval *Register*, which details the priory's expenditure,[4] but there is some evidence from earlier times.

For instance, we know that the kings of England frequently stayed at Thetford. The foundation charter was actually signed by Henry I at Thetford, perhaps in the old cathedral buildings. Later, Henry II's confirmation of the foundation charter was signed at Thetford and Hugh Bigod (first earl of Norfolk and son of the founder) was one of the witnesses.[5] Henry III stayed at Thetford on six different occasions between 1229 and 1245; Edward I on five occasions between 1285 and 1305 and Edward III stayed there twice.[6] It is not certain where the king stayed in Thetford, but the wealthiest religious house in the town, i.e. the Cluniac priory, is by far the most likely; probably the king was accompanied by the priory's patron.

In the time of the Howards we can be more specific. Henry VII stayed at the priory once in 1498–9 and once in 1505–6, several years after the rehabilitation of Thomas Howard (2nd duke) following his brief incarceration in the Tower of London after the Battle of Bosworth. In 1514–15, the prior spent a

---

4   Dymond (ed.), *Register*.
5   J. Caley, H. Ellis, & The Rev. B. Bandinel (eds), W. Dugdale, *Monasticon Anglicanum*, London 1846, V, 150–51.
6   *Calendar of Patent Rolls*, passim.

substantial 11s. 5d. (about 6 days wages for a labourer) on bread, beer, capons and other meat for the duke of Norfolk.[7] The last prior, William Ixworth, had particularly close relations with the Howards, and he can be seen entertaining them frequently, including providing minstrels and jugglers; sometimes the duke's cook did the cooking. The priory was clearly being used by the Howards for formal meetings with third parties, as well as general hospitality and entertainment. In 1527, there was a feast for Thomas Howard (third duke) and · Charles Brandon, duke of Suffolk costing £22 9s. 8d. and including delicacies such as dates, figs, almonds and raisins. Undoubtedly the priory was reimbursed for all these expenses but the *Register*, with rare exceptions, only records outgoings. Unlike today, when a short drive would get us home to Framlingham or Kenninghall after a pleasant dinner, entertainment must also have meant overnight accommodation, probably in the prior's house itself (Fig. 2), or else in a house especially erected for royal and aristocratic guests. There are frequent references to an 'Earl's Hall' in the *Register*, but these are thought to refer to a building in the town, now the site of the King's House. It is perhaps more likely that the prior lodged his high status guests in his own house, immediately west of the church.

Unlike Roger Bigod, the first founder, who only established one monastery (although his successors founded several more), by the time the Norfolk inheritance fell into the hands of the Howards, they had accumulated the patronage of eighteen other houses, including Thetford.[8] Some were richer, some were grander, but it is only Thetford that had this very close relationship with the family. This is partly because of its proximity to the ducal seats of Framlingham Castle and especially Kenninghall, but also because of the long tradition of burial at Thetford Priory.

Burial at the Priory
(with Kirsten Claiden-Yardley)

As we have seen, prayer for their immortal souls was a major reason for members of the nobility to found a religious house. And after their death, there was no better way of ensuring this than having their tombs within sight of the monks of the priory founded by their family and of which they were the patron. Furthermore, their tombs, and those of their family, could be used to impress friends (or enemies) whether through heraldic display, artistic endeavour or the grandeur of the location.

Since patronage of the priory passed from family to family, so burial at 'the abbey', as it was generally known in the Middle Ages and beyond, not only

---

[7]   K. Stöber, *Late Medieval Monasteries and their Patrons, England and Wales, c.1300–1540*, Woodbridge 2007, 176–78.
[8]   Stöber, *Late Medieval Monasteries*, 173.

gained the patron prayers – and thus time off purgatory – but also reinforced their status as an earl or duke of Norfolk (or a close relative of one). It is no accident that the bodies of the most high-born patronal family, that of Thomas of Brotherton, Edward II's half-brother, are not to be found at Thetford; there was no status to be gained by being buried there (Thomas was buried at Bury St Edmunds Abbey). The families before and after, by contrast, reaffirmed their aristocratic position, as well as their piety, by being buried in the Cluniac 'Thetford Abbey', and it is to their burials that we turn now.

The Bigods

The founder, Roger Bigod, died in 1107, shortly after the church on the new site was started and some seven years before it was finished. According to his foundation charter, Roger had wished to be buried there, in the church of his own foundation; the unfinished state of the building would have been no barrier to a temporary grave followed by a translation. However, the first chronicler of Thetford Priory records that Roger's body was seized by the Bishop of Norwich for burial in his own cathedral church. The bishop would not give the body up despite entreaty from his (Roger's) family and friends, and despite the 'great injury' this did to the monks of Thetford.[9] This is a typical medieval story of patronal burial in religious houses: the priories and abbeys wanted their patrons' bodies quite as much the patrons wanted their monks' prayers, and there were numerous disputes involving many religious houses over bodies in the twelfth and thirteenth centuries.

Roger's son and successor, William, drowned in the wreck of the White Ship in November 1120. Writing his *History of Thetford* in the eighteenth century, Thomas Martin avers that all the succeeding Bigods, from William's brother Hugh, the first earl of Norfolk, to Roger the fifth and last Bigod earl (d. 1306), were buried at Thetford Priory.[10] This is likely enough, although only firmly documented for one of them. As founders they would almost certainly have been interred near that place of highest honour, the high altar, either immediately in front of it, if their tombs were flat, or off to one side, between the piers of the arcades, if they were raised (Fig. 3). For the earlier Bigods, at least, the high altar was further west than now, before the east end was lengthened and squared off.[11]

The Mowbrays

The estates of the Norfolk earldom passed through marriage to the Mowbrays in 1375, including the patronage of Thetford Priory. Thomas Mowbray was

---

9   F. Blomefield, *An Essay Towards a Topographical History of the County of Norfolk*, vol. 2, London 1805, 104–5.

10   Martin, *Thetford*, 121.

11   F. J. E Raby & P. K. Baillie Reynolds, *Thetford Priory Norfolk*, London 1979 (first edn 1946).

created the first duke of Norfolk (1397) but died in Venice; his elder son was executed for treason and his next son, Thomas, was buried at Epworth Priory, despite willing his body to be buried at the Carthusian house at Axholme, which he had founded. It was not until the time of the third Mowbray duke of Norfolk that the family took an interest in Thetford as a place of burial. John Mowbray was buried there in 1461, followed by his widow some thirteen years later and then by his son, the last Mowbray duke, who died in 1475/6 at Framlingham Castle. The records do not tell us clearly where any of these Mowbrays were buried. There are signs of two tombs between the piers on each of the north and south sides of the presbytery, and interesting fragments of a suitable date were found in the east end of the church during the excavations of the 1930s. In a deposition regarding the heraldry present in the Howards' priory, made late in 1546 following the arrest of Henry Howard, earl of Surrey and his father Thomas Howard (see Claiden-Yardley's discussion, below), the heraldry of two tombs in the 'quire' is described: one on the left hand side (north) and one on the right hand side (south) as one approaches the high altar. The one on the north side is ascribed to a Mowbray duke, and on the basis of the heraldry may be John Mowbray, who died in 1461, perhaps – speculatively – following wounds received at the battle of Towton earlier that year. The tomb on the south side has often been ascribed to John Howard, duke of Norfolk, who died in 1485. This is on the basis of the 1546 deposition which refers to it as the tomb of Duke Thomas who was killed at King Richard's field (the use of the wrong name has been treated as an error by the original scribe). Closer inspection of the heraldic descriptions suggests that it may not have been a Howard tomb at all. It is more likely that it belonged to another of the Mowbray family.

The Howards

According to a tradition dating back to the sixteenth century, John Howard, the first duke of that name, was buried at Thetford Priory. This is certainly what he desired and, after the creation of the new dukedom in 1483, the priory *Register* shows that a new chapel was being constructed.[12] This must be the chapel on the north side of the nave, in the angle with the north transept, where parts of a fan vault were found in 1849, along with fragments of painted and gilded screen (Fig. 4).[13] Although John was killed while fighting for Richard III at the Battle of Bosworth in 1485, noble combatants on both sides of a battle were usually given an honourable burial, even if it was unusual for their bodies to travel so far. With the architecture, the historical tradition, and the discovery of a grave,

[12] Dymond (ed.), *Register*, 59–60.
[13] H. Harrod, 'Observations on the history and present state of Thetford priory, with a plan,' *Norfolk and Norwich Archaeological Society Transactions*, 3 (1852), 105–24.

it remains reasonable to suppose that John's body was indeed interred in the chapel built for him.

Famously, his son Thomas was buried with great pomp at Thetford in 1524 below a tomb of considerable grandeur (see the Lindley and Gunn/Claiden-Yardley essays), reasonably presumed to be above the large burial vault in the middle of the presbytery ('5' in Fig. 3). As we shall see, the building was adjusted to accommodate it.

From the *Register*, we know that a number of other Howards were buried at Thetford: Lady Anne Howard, first wife of the third duke, who died in 1511 (but work on her grave took place in 1518/19, suggesting a new tomb); and Lord Thomas Howard, brother of the third duke, who died in the Tower of London in 1537. Additionally, the third duke's son-in-law, and natural son of Henry VIII, Henry Fitzroy, was buried in the priory in 1536. Although we know quite a lot about the latter's tomb, we do not know the precise location of any of these burials.

Other Burials

As well as these aristocratic burials, the priory also received the bodies of less exalted and more local individuals. Many of Roger Bigod's men and tenants were persuaded to give gifts to his new monastery, at the time of the foundation, and some of the gifts also specify a request for burial e.g Ralph Fitzwalter and Maud his wife; Alice de Albeni; and Robert de Vaux, whose gift notes that his body is to be buried at Thetford 'as all the rest of the earl's men'. Until the fifteenth century, records are rather sparse, although a chantry in 1300, founded by Richard de Huphall, shows that the priory remained a locus of noble piety, aside from that of the patronal family. Roger Stoppysley (1416) and his mother Dionise (1424), John West of Thetford (1420), John Phelyp (1424) and Roger Swan (1476) were all buried here in the fifteenth century while Robert Love, a former mayor of Thetford, was buried in 1511.[14] The habit of burying the heads of religious houses in their chapter houses had largely died out by the late thirteenth century, and they too were now interred in places of honour within their monastic church.

Without question, the known surviving records document far fewer burials in the priory church and cemetery than actually took place throughout the medieval period. Tellingly, the excavation of Bardney Abbey (Benedictine, Lincolnshire) by Harold Brakspear in 1909, which must have been quickly covered with soil post-Suppression, revealed so many grave slabs that in places they made a continuous monument-floor.[15] The floor of Thetford Priory church may have been similarly covered.

[14]   Blomefield, *Norfolk*, 106 and 126.
[15]   H. Brakspear, 'Bardney Abbey', *Archaeological Journal*, 79 (1922). 1–92.

The Church and the Setting of the Burials

The setting of the burials, of course, was an important Cluniac monastery and within that, the monks' great church. It was not a humble edifice. The monks were well-endowed by Roger Bigod and others but it still took them most of the twelfth century to finish the church, along with numerous other buildings. They ended up with a middling-sized monastic church (about half the length of its huge cathedral neighbours Ely and Norwich) in the mainstream of East of England Romanesque style, with three eastern apses and a further single apsidal chapel off each of the north and south transepts.

Like its Cluniac sister Castle Acre, at the other end of the county, the west front of the nave was finished with twin towers above the aisles. Thetford church is now almost razed to the ground, but the surviving west front at Castle Acre gives a good idea of the quantity and quality of decorative detail there may have been. This impression is greatly strengthened by the numerous carved and moulded voussoirs (arch stones), carved capitals and tympana recovered from the site from the 1930s onwards (Fig. 5). The interior fixtures, fittings and decoration must have been continually maintained and updated but the first significant development of the church building after its completion took place in the mid-13th century with the addition of the lady chapel on the north side of the presbytery (the date principally determined by the surviving remains). This was a standard architectural move following the local, Walsingham-inspired, preference for northern lady chapels; building it in two distinct phases (the eastern half followed by the western) is more unusual. The extension of the presbytery to create a cliff-like square east end took place at almost the same time.

If the building was as smart on the inside as the plan and architectural fragments suggest, then the earls and dukes of Norfolk might well have wanted to be buried there, even without considering familial piety and tradition.

In some instances, we can see how the presence of patronal tombs directly changed the shape of the building in which they were housed. Most obvious is the chapel in the angle of the north transept and nave (with tomb '4' in Fig. 3). As we have already seen, this was covered with a fan vault and enclosed with a painted screen (Fig. 4). The priory only spent £2 8s. 0d. on the chapel, although some small costs might be hidden in general entries. It is highly unlikely that this sum could have covered the cost of the chapel; in 1476, just lengthening the south aisle of Broxbourne church (Herts), making a new arcade arch with a table tomb beneath (no screen and no vault) cost £24, not including the materials.[16] The bulk of the costs, then, are almost certainly hidden by the duke of Norfolk paying the master mason directly; the priory could not be expected to bear the costs of either tombs or buildings or screens created especially for them. For

---

[16]   L. F. Salzman, *Building in England down to 1540*, Oxford 1952, 537–8.

instance, an 'alabaster man' was given 8*d*. in 1501–2, a sum so trivial that it could not possibly have covered the material or the carving (though perhaps the erection) of an alabaster tomb – a handful of fragments of which survive.

A few years later, from 1507 to 1510, there were works on the east gable, including a new east window, the costs coming to (at least) £18 17*s*. 2*d*. In this instance, the priory had substantially paid for the works but is it possible that the redesigned east end, with its new window and substantially raised altar (Fig. 6) was also prompted by Howard tombs? Thomas Howard's massive chest tomb (see Lindley's essay, below) was placed in the centre of the presbytery, potentially completely obscuring the monks' view of the high altar. Seeing the elevation of the host (communion wafers and wine) at mass was very important in the late Middle Ages, and raising the altar solved the problem. However, the new east end was created more than a decade before Thomas Howard's death in 1524. We know from his will (see Claiden-Yardley's essay, below) that he was thinking about his tomb long before his death, even if not as far in advance as 1507. Nonetheless, he may at that time have entered into negotiations with the priory over his place of burial and tomb, prompting their architectural response.

Like many of the tombs, the building itself was ornamented with the heraldry of the different patronal families. The 1546 document records numerous examples of Brotherton and Mowbray arms at the east end of the nave including on the ceiling and in a glass window. The *Register* records a payment, of only 2*s*. 4*d*., in 1528–9 'pro le glazing le armys Domini Ducis Norff'. As with the chapel and tombs, the patrons themselves may have paid the principal costs of embellishing their priory in this way and so this type of work may have been far more common than the extant records suggest.

Acccss to the Church
The burials we know about are clustered towards the east end, along with altars, screens and choir stalls. Proximity to the high altar, to other altars where mass was celebrated, and to the monks' choir stalls, all evinced a greater status, both secular and spiritual. Although, with a suitable gift, almost anyone might be buried in the nave, burial in presbyteries was more restricted. This is true not just of Thetford, but was general ecclesiastical practice. For instance, the Statutes of Chichester in 1292 decreed that there should be no indiscriminate burials in chancels.[17] The restriction on burials in chancels and presbyteries also extended to the living, but once again this depended very much on who you were. From as early as the mid-thirteenth century we can see the formalisation of access. In the statutes written for the Lincoln diocese *c*.1239, the laity is specifically forbidden to stand or sit in the chancel with the clergy during the divine service

[17]   F. M. Powicke & C. R. Cheney (eds), *Councils and Synods: with other Documents Relating to the English Church II A.D. 1205–1313* (2 parts), Oxford 1964.

except only for the patron 'on account of deference or other rational and evident reason'. There is a similar clause in the statutes of Worcester a year later: the laity may not stand in the chancel except for 'revered patrons and exalted persons', and another in the Durham statutes of 1241×1249. The surviving contemporary statutes for Norwich do not address the issue and they are all, in any case, largely aimed at parish churches. Nonetheless, the general intention is clear: if you are the patron of a church or sufficiently exalted, then access to holy areas was not a problem from this time forwards. This outlook is as likely to have spread to, or come from, monastic houses.

For the nobility, this was important. Now they might offer prayers at the tombs of their ancestors, witness the prayers of the monks and, perhaps as importantly, show their friends and peers the stylish tombs and heraldry on display in the monastery of which they were patron. This privilege was probably allowed to the Bigods; for the Mowbrays and Howards, it must have been taken as read. Interestingly, a number of what we might imagine as secular belongings were found (dropped?) in the eastern arm of the church, including tokens and a painted lead rose. Other finds for which we don't know the find-spot, and that might be associated with lay visitors, include harness fittings (Fig. 7) and a pilgrim badge (Fig. 8). The pilgrim badge has an annunciation scene, similar in style to many made at the great Marian pilgrimage centre of Walsingham. It is tempting, though unprovable, to identify the Thetford example either with a badge bought on behalf of John, first Howard duke, or perhaps with one of the many bought for Henry VII and his retinue.[18]

Just as it was a privilege for a lay person to enter the eastern end of the monastic church either alive or dead, so it was a privilege for Thetford Priory to receive the bodies of their aristocratic patrons. Not only did this gain them gifts (the burgess buried in 1511 gave £20 to the prior, £1 to each priest-monk and 10s. to each novice; one presumes that the dukes of Norfolk were more generous) but it would also enhance the reputation of the house. Even today, Thetford's Cluniac priory is remembered principally because the dukes of Norfolk were buried there.

Altars, Screens and Other Fittings

The physical and liturgical environment was an important factor when choosing – or offering – a burial place. The high altar is at the east end of the presbytery and the altar dedicated to Mary in the lady chapel to the north; the two documented tabernacles – one showing the assumption of the Virgin Mary and the other her nativity – were probably also located in or near the lady chapel. A massive statue niche survives in the north transept next to the entrance to the

---

[18] B. Spencer, *Pilgrim Souvenirs and Secular Badges. Medieval Finds from Excavations in London*, London 2010, 135.

lady chapel and this may have housed one of them. Early in the fifteenth century, the monk John Brame recorded the vivid thirteenth-century story of the building of the lady chapel, complete with miracle-working statue of Mary.

The fifteenth- and sixteenth-century *Register* of the priory additionally mentions St Katharine's chapel, the altar of the Holy Trinity, the altar of St Peter, and St Faith's chapel, but does not tell us where they are. The location of further altars, and the monks' stalls, is obvious from the building itself (Fig. 3) but surely neither the visible set nor the documented altars, tabernacles and relics comes close to representing the full quantity of liturgical elements that were present in the church. There may have been altars between the pillars of the nave; there would have been numerous statues, paintings and hangings; chapels (and some tombs) would have been divided off with ornate screens of either timber or stone. While no timber survives, very many fragments of fifteenth- and sixteenth-century stone screen and cornice survive in the English Heritage collections. Although they are too fragmentary to reconstruct, we can say some things about them: some of the cornice fragments were painted red and gold; many were carved with incredible delicacy from Caen Stone imported from Normandy. These included narrow Perpendicular panels with openwork tracery (Fig. 9) and spectacular tiny hollow stone shafts with openwork tracery either spiralling round (Fig. 10) or creating a miniature tower with tier upon tier of miniscule openings. Another hollow, painted, spiral shaft creates a living vine, with roots at the bottom and bunches of grapes at the top (Fig. 11). Locally, work of this delicacy and imagination can be seen in the two chantry chapels at the east end of Ely cathedral, one to Bishop Alcock (built 1480s) and one to Bishop West (completed 1534), the latter a fascinating amalgam of Gothic and Renaissance decorative elements.[19] Nationally, like the Ely chantry chapels, the carving and design at Thetford is on a par with work carried out for the court, at Westminster Abbey or at Hampton Court. Some of the pieces were undoubtedly from screens, guarding the entrance to chapels; others might have enclosed a tomb, perhaps creating space for a private chantry (where priests said daily masses for the soul of the donor). The dainty shafts might have been part of a screen, but equally might have stood on the corners of a tomb slab, supporting a decorative canopy (though they would have needed an iron rod in the middle to do the supporting!). Tiny fragments of painted wall plaster (Fig. 12) show that the building was as brightly coloured and striking as the tombs and screens below. Larger fragments of early Renaissance decorative plaster – but unfortunately we do not know where from – just might indicate the pioneering use of this new technique for one of the tombs or canopies (Fig. 13). Standing in the ruins now, with maybe two dozen boxes of fragments, it is hard to picture the glory that was.

---

[19]   J. Maddison, *Ely Cathedral. Design and Meaning*, Ely 2000, 95–101.

Carved in wood, fixtures and fittings such as these would have been costly; carved in stone, a more intractable, brittle and expensive material, they would have been even dearer. Fittings associated with particular tombs would have been paid for by the family or owner of the tomb; other work will have been paid directly by the priory, even if it was actually paid for by a gift. Thus, the priory *Register* is only partially helpful on this point, since on the one hand it only records outgoings and not income, and on the other hand, many of the entries are too general to be identified with any particular tomb or screen.

The Dissolution at Thetford

On the eve of the Dissolution, Thetford Priory church was in a good state of repair, with many new tombs and screens, brightly coloured walls, new windows, wall hangings and new tile floors. Maintenance and repair had taken place throughout the rest of the monastery, with considerable money spent on the kitchens, bakehouse and prior's lodging, for example. New covered ways had recently been provided round the cloister and from the cloister to the infirmary. The infirmary itself (apart from its early thirteenth-century chapel) is no earlier than the fifteenth century and is clearly divided into separate chambers, each with its own fireplace and latrine, probably for the occupation of either elderly or senior monks.

The good upkeep of the buildings and the priory's active relationship with its patrons proved, in the end, to be irrelevant. After Henry VIII had declared himself Supreme Head of the church in England in 1532, the writing was on the wall. Always in need of money, and urged on by more radical religious reformers than himself, the dissolution of the monasteries was at hand, and not even Thomas Howard's appeal to Henry VIII to keep the church saved Thetford (see Lindley, below), although it was one of the very last to surrender, as late as 16 February 1540.

The priory escaped the first main wave of Dissolution, in the first place because it had more than 12 monks and then because it had an annual income of more than £200. It was the first Act, though, that established the principle of destruction: either the Suppression Commissioners, or the first private owners of each former monastery, after the immediate removal of plate and treasures, and lead from the roofs, for the king's use, were required to 'pull down to the ground all the walls of the churches, stepulls, cloysters, fraterys, dorters, chapter howys'[20] so that religious life could not be re-established.

The evidence at Thetford could suggest that by 1540, either the ardour for destruction had diminished somewhat, or that no-one was checking and the new owners could please themselves. As with so many of the dissolved religious

---

[20]   D. Knowles, *The Religious Orders in England. Vol. 3 The Tudor Age*, Cambridge 1959, 384.

houses of Norfolk, the priory came into the hands of Thomas Howard – as a consequence of the Dissolution, he doubled his landholdings in Norfolk alone.[21] At the same time, the remaining four religious houses of Thetford were purchased by Richard Fulmerston, a high-ranking servant of the Howard family, who spoke up for Thomas after his arrest (Fig. 14).[22] Thus, all the principal religious houses of the town (and, indeed most of the hospitals) were in sympathetic hands.

A stroll around the priory today shows that it did, ultimately, suffer the same fate as the majority of religious houses. Nonetheless, there are good reasons to suppose that this was not the result of immediate and deliberate slighting. On the one hand, later engravings (Fig. 15) and documentary evidence show that much of the demolition work took place in the eighteenth century. On the other, in the 1546 heraldic survey of Thetford Priory (see Claiden-Yardley, below), made immediately after Thomas Howard and his eldest son's incarceration in the Tower of London, it is clear that at least one ceiling was still intact. Once a roof has gone, ceilings follow shortly afterwards, and it is tempting to presume that Thomas Howard still had some affection for the priory or, at the very least, his ancestors' tombs (even though his father's body may already have been moved to Lambeth by then;[23] see Lindley, below).

Elsewhere in Thetford, the churches of the religious houses owned by Richard Fulmerston may similarly have been spared immediate slighting. A convincing case has been made for the chancel of the Dominican friary (also called Thetford Priory) surviving into the seventeenth century.[24] Very little is known about the fate of the Austin friary, but we know that Fulmerston preserved the churches of the other two religious houses he acquired: the church of the canons of the Holy Sepulchre, which was in use as a barn in the eighteenth century and the church of the Benedictine nunnery of St George, turned into a house ('The Place') and now the home of the British Trust for Ornithology.

Thus, the immediate preservation of the churches of the religious houses of Thetford following their dissolution may be intimately connected with Howard patronage: patronage both of the priory and personal patronage of a family friend.

---

[21] T. H. Swales, 'The Redistribution of the Monastic Lands in Norfolk at the Dissolution', *Norfolk Archaeology*, 34 (1966), 14–44.

[22] Dymond (ed.), *Register*, 59; David M. Head, *The Ebbs and Flows of Fortune: the Life of Thomas Howard, Third Duke of Norfolk*, Athens GA 1995; *Letters and Papers of Henry VIII*, 21/2, 280–82.

[23] Richard Marks, 'The Howard tombs at Thetford and Framlingham: new discoveries', *The Archaeological Journal* 141 (1984), 252–68.

[24] C. Norton, D. Park and P. Binski, *Dominican Painting in East Anglia. The Thornham Parva Retable and the Musée de Cluny Frontal*, Woodbridge 1987, 92–5.

Rediscovery

The existence of the Cluniac priory was never forgotten – it lived on both as ruins and as the working 'Abbey Farm', which occupied the old prior's lodging, immediately west of the church. Even this was unroofed in 1737, not far off the period when antiquarian interest in the priory took off in earnest, mainly in the hands of Norfolk historians Thomas Martin and Francis Blomefield. Thomas Martin's interest led him not only to study the numerous medieval documents, but even to excavate 'a trench across the choir, about three yards from the altar [where he] found a large stone coffin with a skeleton of either a Bigod or a prior' – this would make the coffin somewhere between the second Howard duke's tomb (no 5 on plan) and the east end, but if so this has not been rediscovered.

Much of the stonework was taken down for reuse in the early eighteenth century and numerous engravings and photographs from the late seventeenth to the twentieth centuries give a vivid appearance of the priory's decline (Figs 16–17), while at the same time the ground level around it was rising. A large pit (of uncertain purpose) was dug in the centre of the cloister by the farm tenants. In 1849, Henry Harrod had to negotiate 'huge masses of fallen wall' and in places a depth of 12 feet of rubble and other material above the floor level, in order to excavate two long trenches north-south and east-west through the church.[25] The situation had not significantly changed by 1930 when the church and claustral buildings were acquired by the Crown, as can be seen in Fig. 17. By 1934, clearance excavations had begun (Fig. 18). As was usual, excavations stopped at the highest medieval floor level, without any systematic recording at all of post-Dissolution features and, indeed, many post-medieval features were destroyed. However, finds were fairly carefully recorded with a brief description and a grid reference to locate it; the finds sheets survive, but in the intervening 80 years the matching documentation on the objects has been largely lost. Nonetheless, about 20% of them (336) have been identified in the current English Heritage collection.

The single most important group was found immediately north of the north transept, in the building known as the sacristy (Fig. 3), and comprised up to 70 pieces or fragments of fine early Renaissance sculpture, many matching the Howard tombs now in Framlingham church, and discussed in more detail here by Phillip Lindley. Also of considerable interest, were the hundreds of fragments found in the presbytery. Many of these were actually found inside the brick vault of Thomas Howard's tomb, and they included tomb and heraldic fragments, fragments of screen, including the miniature carved openwork shafts discussed above, but also a considerable quantity of window tracery. Very generally, the screen and tomb fragments, while often badly damaged, are very little worn. By

[25] Harrod, 'Thetford Priory', 114–17.

contrast, many of the window fragments are badly worn as well as broken; all the located window fragments were also found within the tomb rather than spread around the presbytery or elsewhere. Although this might only be indicative of the survival of 1930s markings on the material, it could suggest that one or more of the windows (perhaps the new east window constructed in 1507–10) was still standing and open to the elements before falling and being swept away into the open tomb.

Summary
Thetford Priory is a complex site, and only the church has been looked at in any detail here. Despite its decline, it is clear that the priory remained in good condition until 1540 and, in places, beyond that. Throughout its history as an active monastery, the relationship between the prior and its patrons was crucial. Patronage influenced its wealth and standing; the development and appearance of some of the buildings, especially the church. And patronage delayed the priory's demise and played a part in the priory's early post-Dissolution history. Though primarily a religious house, Thetford Priory was connected to and affected by all the currents of the secular world as well.

Tudor Noble Funerals

KIRSTEN CLAIDEN-YARDLEY

The funeral in Tudor England served both religious and social purposes. In the pre-Reformation period there was an intercessory function to the service, as it was one of a number of methods of seeking prayers for the soul of the deceased.[1] The theological changes of the Reformation, in particular the assault on the doctrine of purgatory during the late 1540s, meant the removal of those elements from the funeral; the result was that services now focused primarily on the living rather than assisting the dead.[2] They were intended to provide instruction on divine judgement and resurrection given the inevitability of death, a fate for which the living needed to prepare. Funerals also had a role to play for English society as a whole. On a personal level, they offered an opportunity for family, friends, neighbours, tenants and household to gather and pay their respects to the deceased. They also enabled the expression of aspects of noble identity such as status, kinship, local influence and service. By considering funerals across the period it is possible to see both change but also considerable continuity of purpose.

Status

During the seventeenth century, the nobility of England became increasingly disenchanted with elaborate, heraldic funerals but in the sixteenth century the ceremonies were still very much under the control of the heralds of the College of Arms.[3] The heralds dictated how much black cloth was used to make gowns for those attending, based on their rank; oversaw the painting of the various heraldic banners and decorations; organised the procession; and, through their attendance, represented royal authority. In return, they received a substantial fee.[4] The funeral was designed to ensure that the status of the deceased, and of those attending, was recognised, that social order was seen to be maintained and that noble 'virtues' were displayed. The concern with using the correct ceremonials for the deceased's status was evident at the funeral of William Courtenay, earl of Devon in 1511 when, by the King's commandment, he was

1   Eamon Duffy, *The Stripping of the Altars. Traditional Religion in England c. 1400– c. 1580*, New Haven and London 1992, 338.
2   Ibid., 454–6; Ralph Houlbrooke, 'Death, Church, and Family in England between the Late Fifteenth and the Early Eighteenth Centuries', in *Death, Ritual, and Bereavement*, ed. Ralph Houlbrooke, London and New York 1989, 34.
3   Clare Gittings, *Death, Burial and the Individual in Early Modern England*, London 1988, 188.
4   Ibid., 171–4, 81–2.

named an earl so that he could be buried as one, even though he had died before his ceremonial investiture.[5]

The provision of a funeral feast maintained the social order because the heir was renewing relationships that might have been altered by the previous title-holder's death and displaying his continued wealth and power. As this function of the funeral was not rooted in religious doctrine, we see continuity between Catholic and Protestant funerals. At the funeral of Thomas Howard, second duke of Norfolk in 1524, four-hundred messes of food were laid on, enough to feed up to one thousand six-hundred people. After Francis Talbot, fifth earl of Shrewsbury's funeral in 1560, 320 messes were provided to 'all manner of people who seemed honest'. Leftover food was distributed to the poor and supplemented by the distribution of a dole, normally of 2*d*. per person. At the funeral of Henry Percy, fourth earl of Northumberland in 1489, 14,800 people received the dole and at the second duke of Norfolk's funeral, £100 was shared between 12,000 poor people.[6] The distribution of alms had been seen as aiding the deceased's soul in purgatory but it continued after the abolition of purgatory, in part because Protestant teaching looked favourably on alms-giving.[7] Thus, the leftovers distributed at the fifth earl of Shrewsbury's funeral were accompanied by a dole of 2*d*. per person.[8]

Kinship and Ancestry

The maintenance or advancement of noble status was rooted in kinship deriving either from an individual's ancestors or advantageous marriage alliances. As a result there was an intense pride in illustrious relatives and the privileges that had been inherited from them. Funerals provided an opportunity to display family ties conspicuously through heraldry and to gather an array of the deceased's kin in one place. At the time of his death in 1524, the second duke of Norfolk had a large number of living relatives and this is reflected in the fact that the nine principal mourners at his funeral were primarily drawn from his family – three were his sons and a further four were sons-in-law. Those above the rank of a banneret were entitled to have carried in their funeral procession both a standard and a banner of arms, the dimensions of the standard being determined by their rank.[9] In addition bannerolls of arms, penselles (small

---

5 College of Arms, MS 1.3, f. 33v.

6 Francis Peck, *Desiderata Curiosa: Or, a Collection of Divers Scarce and Curious Pieces (Relating Chiefly to Matters of English History) in Six Books*, London 1779, vol. 2, 247; Thomas Martin, *The History of the Town of Thetford in the Counties of Norfolk and Suffolk, from the Earliest Accounts to the Present Time*, London 1779, App. 43; College of Arms, MS I.7, f. 60r.

7 Houlbrooke, 'Death, Church, and Family', 35.

8 Peck, *Desiderata Curiosa*, vol. 2, 247.

9 John Gough Nichols (ed.), *The Diary of Henry Machyn, Citizen and Merchant-*

heraldic flags) and painted escutcheons of arms would be displayed around the hearse and church. The heraldic achievements that would be offered during the funeral brought together heraldry and personal items of service such as the helmet and sword (although these were normally replicas made for the funeral).

The amount of heraldic paraphernalia was often extensive and, as with displays of status, was unaffected by religious changes. Thomas Howard, third duke of Norfolk, who died in 1554, had twelve bannerrolls of his ancestry, twelve dozen penselles and twelve dozen escutcheons.[10] In 1572, the hearse constructed for Edward Stanley, third earl of Derby was liberally decorated with a hatchment of his arms, escutcheons and penselles whilst the black fabric hung in the church was emblazoned with escutcheons of his arms and marriages and six bannerrolls of his ancestry and marriages were carried in the funeral procession.[11] The use of family heraldry stressed the continued lineage, even in the face of individual death, further bolstering the existing social order.[12]

Service
The nobility had a military and political function to play and it was expected that they would serve their King loyally. That could mean acting as a councillor, sitting in the House of Lords, waiting on the King in the privy chamber, holding an office of state or providing military support.[13] The presence of the heralds, as royal representatives, at noble funerals signified that the deceased had died honourably as a loyal servant of the crown.[14] The sixteenth century also saw alterations in the nature of noble service with the emergence of new noblemen who had risen through the administrative ranks. Just as there were different types of service, so there were different means of expressing that service within the funeral. In some cases the principal mourners at a funeral were representative of the deceased's service. When Thomas, Lord Wharton died in 1568, his mourners were drawn from the ranks of the Tudor administrators with whom he had worked in the North of England.[15] A similar display was evident at the funeral of Charles Brandon, duke of Suffolk, in 1545. His mourners were primarily men who had served with him in war, particularly on the 1544 Boulogne campaign.[16]

Taylor of London from A.D. 1550 to A.D. 1563, London 1848, pp. xxvi–xxvii.
[10]   Ibid., 70.
[11]   Bodleian Library, MS Ashmole 836, ff. 216, 218–19.
[12]   Mervyn James, 'Two Tudor Funerals,' in *Society, Politics and Culture, Studies in Early Modern England*, ed. Mervyn James, *Past and Present Publications*, Cambridge 1986, 177.
[13]   Helen Miller, *Henry VIII and the English Nobility*, Oxford 1986, 255.
[14]   Gittings, *Death, Burial and the Individual*, 174.
[15]   James, 'Two Tudor Funerals', 186.
[16]   S. J. Gunn, *Charles Brandon Duke of Suffolk 1484–1545*, Oxford 1988, 192.

There are examples of funeral sermons being used to make references to an individual's service, although these are rare. The second duke of Norfolk's funeral sermon approached the question of service with the theme of 'Behold the lion of the Tribe of Judah triumphs', a reference to the highly successful military service that had been key to securing his restoration to his father's titles.[17] As well as sermons, proclamations of the deceased's titles were made by the heralds during the funeral and highlighted loyal service. In 1572, it was declared that William Paulet, marquis of Winchester, had been 'a most Worthy counseller to the princes of famous memory ... whome he had loyally servid' and the offices that he had held were listed.[18] More generally, the noble funeral included the display and offering of the achievements, that is to say the helm and crest, sword, target (shield) and the coat of arms (tabard decorated with the coat of arms). The heraldry meant that they were symbols of the deceased's lineage but they were also symbols of chivalric, military service. They were included at Winchester's funeral even though he had risen through administrative service, suggesting that the achievements were symbols of rank based on idealised notions of noble service rather than the actual service rendered.

Local Influence

One form of service undertaken by most noblemen was representing royal government in the localities. This could mean being appointed to commissions or to offices such as President of the Council of the North. They were also expected to take a lead in times of crisis in the localities. The importance of their local influence can be seen in the history of sixteenth-century rebellion. In 1525 rebellions broke out in East Anglia over the Amicable Grant taxation and the dukes of Norfolk and Suffolk acted together to contain the unrest.[19] In contrast, when popular uprisings broke out across England in 1549, there were no influential noblemen in East Anglia and the south-west, meaning armies had to be brought in from other counties to put down the rebellions.[20] As well as acting for the Crown, the nobility also provided a route to office holding, rewards and justice for people in the area where they exercised power. Those that did this well built up personal ties with kin, servants and neighbours. The strength of these ties is evident in the number of noblemen choosing burial near to their principal houses. This included the Howards who requested burial at Thetford,

---

[17] W. A. Sessions, *Henry Howard the Poet Earl of Surrey: A Life*, Oxford 1999, 19.

[18] Bodleian Library, MS Ashmole 836, f. 214.

[19] Diarmaid MacCulloch, *Suffolk and the Tudors. Politics and Religion in an English County 1500–1600*, Oxford 1986, 60–1.

[20] Diarmaid MacCulloch, 'Kett's Rebellion in Context,' *Past & Present* 84 (1979), 43; Helen Speight, 'Local Government in the South-Western Rising of 1549,' *Southern History* 18 (1996), 1–3.

and subsequently, Framlingham, which were at the heart of their primary area of influence. As a spectacle, the funeral processions would have been difficult to miss and clearly demonstrated the continuing power of the nobility. Based on the evidence of the number of black gowns distributed, we can tell that both John de Vere, 13th earl of Oxford and the 2nd duke of Norfolk had around 900 laymen at their funeral in addition to hundreds of friars, priests and clerks.[21]

The importance of funerals as a display of noble power in the localities was recognised by Queen Elizabeth and her Secretary William Cecil, Lord Burghley who intervened to force noble funerals to be held in the country rather than in London.[22] As has been observed, the principal mourners could reflect family and service networks, but they could also represent local connections. Looking at the funerals of Henry, Lord Marney, John de Vere, 13th earl of Oxford and the 2nd duke of Norfolk we see that the chief mourner for the 13th earl of Oxford was his heir, the 14th earl, who was also a mourner for Norfolk eleven years later. Sir William Waldegrave, an Essex man, was a mourner for John de Vere and Henry Marney. The Lords Willoughby and Fitzwalter, both East Anglian land owners, were mourners both for John de Vere and Thomas Howard. Of Marney's remaining mourners, Wentworth, Tyrrell and Tey all received annuities in the will of the 13th earl of Oxford. By comparing the funerals we are able to build up a picture of interlinking networks in Essex and East Anglia during the first decades of Henry VIII's reign.[23]

Religion

It can be difficult to determine the precise religious beliefs of sixteenth-century noblemen, particularly during the theological confusion in the middle of the century. However, whilst there were changes in the forms of Christian worship and the details of doctrine, there was a continued expectation that noblemen would be exemplars of piety. Understandably given their public nature, funerals appear to conform to royal religious policies rather than serve as overt statements of opposition. In part this is because there was a standard structure, the main alterations to which were driven by theological changes. The dissolution of the monasteries and friaries meant that funeral processions could no longer be led by the orders of the friars. The banners of saints carried at each corner of the body lasted longer, appearing at Suffolk's funeral in 1545, but they were then dispensed with. The theological reforms of Edward VI's reign meant fewer services took place as part of the funeral, and the herald's proclamation of the

21 College of Arms, MS I.7, f. 45v, MS I.7, f. 60r.
22 Gittings, *Death, Burial and the Individual*, 168–9.
23 College of Arms, MS I.7, f. 50v; College of Arms, MS I.7, f. 45v; Martin, *Thetford*, App. 39; James Ross, *John De Vere Thirteenth Earl of Oxford 1442–1413*, Woodbridge 2011, 236–7.

deceased's titles no longer began with an admonition to pray for his soul. Meanwhile, sermons became a Protestant means of commemorating the deceased by holding them up as exemplars for the education of the living. By the end of Elizabeth's reign, sermons were increasingly being printed to providing a lasting memorial.[24]

Although the religious structure of a funeral was largely prescribed there was some scope for personalisation. When banners of images were still being carried, three banners were usually reserved for St George, Our Lady and the Trinity. The fourth banner was open to personal choice, for example, at Suffolk's funeral it depicted St Barbara who was the patron saint of artillery and in keeping with Brandon's military image.[25] There was also variation in the people giving the sermons. In the mid-Tudor period, the choice of preacher could throw up some unexpected combinations. Thus in 1550, at the funeral of Thomas Wriothesley, earl of Southampton, who had frequently supported religious conservatives, the sermon is said to have been delivered by John Hooper, a Protestant preacher. This has been interpreted in conjunction with his patronage of reformers, criticism of bishops and destruction of shrines and tombs as evidence of Protestant sympathies on Southampton's part despite his traditional Catholic reputation.[26] However, given a general tendency in commemoration towards religious conformity, it could equally be a reflection of the favoured preachers at the time of his death. Similarly when John Russell, earl of Bedford, died in 1555 the sermon was given by the dean of St Paul's at that time, John Feckenham, Queen Mary's chaplain. As Russell was a religious pragmatist, this probably reflects his personal friendship with Feckenham and, again, the prevailing religious policy, rather than profound counter-reformation tendencies on his part.

The Funeral of Thomas Howard, Second Duke of Norfolk

The funeral of Thomas Howard, second duke of Norfolk which took place at Thetford priory is a particularly good example of a Tudor noble funeral.[27] We have a full description of the leading participants, the pre-Reformation funeral proceedings and the expenditure, but it is important to remember that it was at the top end of the scale in terms of cost and magnificence.

---

[24] Peter Marshall, *Beliefs and the Dead in Reformation England*, Oxford 2002, 165–8.

[25] Bodleian Library, MS Ashmole 1109, f. 144r.

[26] Michael A. R. Graves, 'Wriothesley, Thomas, first Earl of Southampton. (1505–1550)', *Oxford Dictionary of National Biography*, Oxford University Press, 2004; online edn, Jan 2008 [http://www.oxforddnb.com/view/article/30076, accessed 25 Feb 2013].

[27] The manuscript copy of the second duke of Norfolk's funeral is in the College of Arms, MS I.7, ff. 56r–60v. A copy is in Martin, *Thetford*, App. 38–43 but the language has been altered and there are some inaccuracies.

In the days immediately following his death, his body was laid out in his chapel at Framlingham Castle and the buildings decked with black cloth. Then, on 22nd June 1524, a month after he died, the procession was assembled to accompany the body to its final resting place. It was led by the orders of friars in 'coaches', and other religious personages, followed by the men and officers of the duke's household two of whom carried his standard and his banner. The heraldic achievements – helmet and crest, coat of arms, and target of arms – were carried by the heralds. The body was transported on a chariot surrounded by four-hundred burning torches and was followed by the chief mourner (the new duke of Norfolk) supported by a further eight mourners. Completing the procession were nine-hundred lords, knights, and gentlemen, all dressed in black gowns.

Inevitably, the procession was slow moving and took two days to travel from Framlingham to Thetford with the body resting overnight in the church at Diss, where a mass was held. The next morning another mass was held before the procession set off again. At every town or village they passed, they were met with a procession and the church was given five escutcheons of his arms and 6s. 8d. When they reached Thetford, the body was placed within a hearse which was hung with black cloth, trimmed with silk, lit with seven hundred tapers and decorated with coats of arms and banners showing his ancestry and marriages. The following morning, everyone gathered at the priory at 6 a.m. for the first of three masses. The third of these was the mass of Requiem which was sung by the bishop of Ely and during which the principal mourners each offered 10s. Then the supporting mourners offered the heraldic achievements which were passed by the heralds to the duke's heir, symbolising the transfer of power from father to son. They were set aside to be hung in the church once the funeral had finished. That finished, a knight on horseback rode through the church to make an offering of the deceased's battle-axe. The final part of the rituals involved the heralds delivering palls of cloth of gold to the nine mourners who offered them to the hearse. An hour long sermon was delivered before the mourners retired to their chambers. The heralds then proclaimed the titles and offices of the deceased before the body was lowered into the grave. The duke's household officers broke their staves of office and threw them into the grave, the bishop scattered holy water into it and, with great lamentation, the funeral ceremony ended.

With the religious and ceremonial elements of the funeral out of the way, the focus shifted to fulfilling the duties expected of a nobleman. Alms were distributed to the poor and the three hundred priests who had sung masses over the course of the three days were rewarded with 12d. and their dinner. In addition a magnificent entertainment was laid on. Structurally, the funeral was similar to other noble funerals of the time and to sixteenth-century royal funerals which bore a distinct resemblance to noble funerals both in terms of the order of proceedings and the prominence of the deceased's heraldry.[28] In total, Norfolk's funeral cost £1340, a figure that represented around half the duke's total annual landed income. It is not possible to carry out an exact comparison of the total cost of Tudor funerals, but it seems probable that, in real terms, this was one of the most expensive noble funerals of the period. Allowing for inflation, comparable funerals would have been those of Henry Percy, fourth earl of Northumberland which cost £1037 in 1489 and Robert Dudley, earl of Leicester which cost £3500 in 1588.[29] This was a level of expenditure that was verging on royal as it was similar to that spent on the 1503 interment of Prince Arthur and indeed in some areas, such as the provision of black gowns, the Howards outspent the royal family.[30] The temporary display of power and the ideal noble virtues in the funeral were perpetuated through the erection of a tomb monument at Thetford Priory. This was accompanied by a lengthy epitaph that was displayed alongside the tomb and extolled the duke's career and achievements.

Conclusion

The range of functions of a funeral meant that noblemen's funerals reflected both the prevailing religion and a number of important aspects of 'nobility'. They enabled the deceased's representatives to fulfil their expected duties to society by distributing alms, food and drink, and, sometimes, black gowns. The expenditure involved meant they served as a reminder of the deceased's wealth and power whilst the structure and trappings of the ceremony were designed to indicate their position within society and, in many cases, the kinship which legitimised their rank. The heir would normally play a prominent role in the ritual aspects of the funeral representing the transfer of the wealth and power between the generations, and the continuation of the natural social order. It was also possible to use the funeral to celebrate the service done by the deceased for his monarch and country.

Whilst there were changes to funerals over the course of the sixteenth century, particularly in terms of the expression of religious ideas and beliefs, there was also considerable continuity because of their social functions. Although stripped of their Catholic elements, the order of proceedings at the funerals of the earl of Shrewsbury in 1560 or the earl of Derby in 1572 would have been recognisable to their pre-Reformation ancestors. The spread of Protestant ideas

---

[28] Jennifer Loach, 'The Function of Ceremonial in the Reign of Henry VIII,' *Past & Present* 142, no. 1 (1994), 60, 64–6.

[29] Gittings, *Death, Burial and the Individual*, 180.

[30] Ralph Houlbrooke, 'Prince Arthur's Funeral,' in *Arthur Tudor Prince of Wales. Life, Death and Commemoration*, ed. Steven Gunn and Linda Monckton, Woodbridge 2009, 67, 70; Gittings, *Death, Burial and the Individual*, 180.

led to increased criticism of excessive pomp in funerals but the nobility retained their concern for status and, as a result continued to favour expensive funerals.[31] However, whilst the scale and grandeur remained unaffected, seventeenth-century funerals were increasingly a private affair that is to say that they were arranged without reference to the heralds and with a restricted guest list.[32] One result of this was the rise in popularity of night funerals. These allowed the funeral to be arranged quickly without the expense of a cross-country procession, pre-empted any royal interference in the choice of burial location and meant that the choice of mourners was about personal ties rather than having people of the correct ranks, as dictated by the heralds.[33] Alterations in funeral structure and procedure can therefore by seen to have been driven more by a complex relationship between religious ideas, practicalities and cultural change over the period, than simply by the theological changes of the Reformation.

[31]   David Cressy, *Birth, Marriage, and Death. Ritual, Religion, and the Life-Cycle in Tudor and Stuart England,* Oxford 1997, 412–13.
[32]   Ibid., 447, 449–50.
[33]   Gittings, *Death, Burial and the Individual,* 191.

Materiality, Movement and the Historical Moment

PHILLIP LINDLEY

Who lyst his welthe and eas Retayne,
Hym selffe let hym vnknowne contayne;.
Presse not to ffast in at that gatte
Wher the Retorne standes by desdayne:
For sure, circa Regna tonat.[1]

On the afternoon of the twelfth of December 1546, a party of horsemen clattered out of Whitehall Palace on secret royal business, heading for Kenninghall in Norfolk. Riding the distance of some eighty miles at a punishing pace, they arrived before dawn on the fourteenth. At Kenninghall, the duke of Norfolk's great country house, they seized his household, including Norfolk's daughter, Mary, dowager duchess of Richmond, and his mistress, Elizabeth Holland, sending them back to court for interrogation.[2] This was the shocking way that the women and household first heard about the arrests of Thomas Howard, the third duke – the premier nobleman under King Henry VIII – and of his son and heir, the earl of Surrey. Some days later, after receiving further instructions, several of the horsemen forced their way into the abandoned church of the Cluniac Priory in Thetford, the burial place of the Howard dukes and of their predecessors until the monastery's dissolution in 1540. There, they drew up a report on the heraldry displayed on some of the tomb-monuments and sent it back to court.[3] This strange task was an ominous portent for the future of the Howards. Although Norfolk and Surrey may not yet have realised it, the lethal end-game to control the succession after Henry VIII's reign had begun.

A group gathered round Edward Seymour, earl of Hertford, had ruthlessly ousted Norfolk from power.[4] The duke's position had been fatally undermined by his son's arrogance in conspicuously displaying heraldry to which he was fully entitled but which – Surrey had already been warned – could be interpreted as threatening the position of Henry's sickly young heir, the future Edward VI.

---

[1] K. Muir & P. Thomson (eds), *Collected Poems of Sir Thomas Wyatt*, Liverpool 1969, CLXXVI (187).

[2] P. R. Moore, 'The Heraldic Charge against the Earl of Surrey, 1546–47,' *English Historical Review*, 116 (2001), 557–83.

[3] See Kirsten Claiden-Yardley's essay on the 1546 report, below: she points out that stained glass, painted and sculpted representations were also noted. This proves that the church was still preserved at this date.

[4] The nature of the group gathered round Seymour in a temporary alliance to destroy Surrey and his father is examined by S. Brigden, 'Henry Howard, Earl of Surrey, and the "Conjured League",' *Historical Journal*, (37 / 3) 1994, 507–37.

On the morning of the twelfth of December, Duke Thomas had been arrested and his son, Henry Howard, earl of Surrey, poet and soldier, ignominiously led on foot from the house of the Lord Chancellor, Sir Thomas Wriothesley, where he had already been detained, to the Tower of London.[5] The coup headed by the Seymours and Wriothesley was brutal and decisive, but the charges which would destroy the Howards were still inchoate and incoherent. In the end, Surrey and Norfolk were to be convicted of treasonably incorporating royal heraldry into their coats of arms.[6] The case against Surrey was rapidly concocted and almost entirely spurious, as he angrily protested at his trial, but he was nonetheless found guilty and condemned. The earl was beheaded on 19 January 1547. His father abjectly confessed to transparently false charges in the forlorn hope that the king would spare him, but he too was convicted of treason and condemned to death. The duke only escaped execution because Henry VIII himself died in the early hours of 28 January 1547, the day set aside for Norfolk's judicial murder. Too eminent to execute but too powerful to release, Thomas Howard spent the whole of Edward VI's reign (1547–53) incarcerated in the Tower.[7] His forfeited house and many of his estates were given to Mary Tudor. It was no coincidence that she launched her bid for the throne from Kenninghall nor that she gathered her forces at his great castle in Framlingham.[8] In August 1553, Howard was swiftly freed and pardoned by the queen and restored to the Privy Council. The duke officiated at Mary's coronation on 1 October 1553 and presided at her coronation banquet. In both offices he was assisted by his sixteen-year-old grandson, the future fourth duke. An increasingly frail octogenarian, the third duke died at Kenninghall on 25 August 1554. Before his death, he had regained his position and recovered many of his plundered lands; but the pride and ambition which had contributed to his son's downfall would also destroy his grandson. The fourth duke aspired to marry Mary, Queen of Scots, treasonably deceiving Elizabeth I, and was implicated in the Ridolfi plot. He became the third Howard generation in succession to be tried, convicted of treason and condemned to death. Ignominiously degraded from the Order of the Garter – his banner of arms, mantles, helm, and crest were ceremonially thrown into Windsor Castle's ditch – Thomas Howard, fourth duke of Norfolk, was

---

5   Thomas Wriothesley (1505–50), grandson of John Writhe, Garter King of Arms. See Michael A.R. Graves's entry in *Oxford Dictionary of National Biography* [hereafter *ODNB*].

6   Moore, 'Heraldic Charge', 559.

7   D. M. Head, *The Ebbs and Flows of Fortune: The Life of Thomas Howard, Third Duke of Norfolk*, Athens, Georgia, 1995, 228, suggests that Hertford was 'busy with more pressing affairs' and expected the seventy-three year old Howard to die in prison of natural causes.

8   D. MacCulloch, *Suffolk and the Tudors*, Oxford 1986, 79–82. Kenninghall is strategically situated about a dozen miles from Thetford.

beheaded on 2 June 1572 and buried in St Peter ad Vincula in the Tower of London.[9]

Most modern visitors to the tranquil parish church of St Michael, in Framlingham, Suffolk, will be unaware of the connection between these tumultuous events and the remarkable tomb-monuments of the Howard family which stand in the chancel. Yet, as we shall see, the turbulent history of the Howards' perilous relationship with the Tudor monarchs can be read into, and out from, the monuments. Four date from the sixteenth century: the fifth, commemorating the earl of Surrey, is a retrospective work, dated by its inscription to 1614.[10] Unlike the last, none of the earlier monuments bears an inscription. They are usually identified as commemorating:

1. Thomas, the third Howard duke of Norfolk (d. 1554), and his first wife, Anne (d. 1511), daughter of Edward IV (Figs 1–3);[11]
2. Henry Fitzroy, duke of Richmond & Somerset (d. 1536) and his wife Duchess Mary [Howard] (d. 1555) (Figs 4–6);
3. Duchesses Mary Fitzalan (d. 25 August 1557) and Margaret Audley (d. 10 January 1564), the first two of the three wives of Thomas Howard, the fourth duke (d. 1572) (Fig. 7);
4. Finally, the fourth duke's daughter, Elizabeth Howard (d. c. 1565) (Fig. 8).

The first is ascribed to the third duke on the basis of its recumbent effigies of the duke and his wife; Richmond's is identified by its heraldry, since there are no effigies on its tomb-chest; the third monument can be confidently assigned on the basis of its heraldry and the presence of the effigies of the fourth duke's first two wives; the final one is less securely attributed, because it bears neither effigy nor heraldry.

These perplexing absences – of inscriptions and/or effigies – raise serious questions which only increase in number when the format, style and iconography of the monuments are considered. The first two are freestanding, the third

---

[9] *ODNB* entry by Michael A. R. Graves. For a detailed examination of the Howards' relationship to the Tudors, see the essay by Dr Gunn and Kirsten Claiden-Yardley, above.

[10] This is the subject of Dr Ford's essay, below.

[11] The *ODNB* entry on the third duke by Graves, indicating that this effigy represents the second duchess, appears to follow the nineteenth-century church guide by Green, discussed below. However, she was buried at Lambeth (according to Graves's own *ODNB* entry on her). It seems anyway very unlikely, given their well-known animosity, that she would be represented beside her estranged husband at Framlingham, in spite of the fact that they were reconciled after 1553, according to Head, *Ebbs and Flows*, 244. The salient fact is that he left her nothing in his will. The woman represented is, with near certainty, duchess Anne, who had been buried at Thetford.

adjoins the north wall of the chancel's aisle; the fourth is a small wall-monument, set slightly to the west of the last, against the north aisle wall. It will be Richmond's and the third duke's monuments with which we shall be primarily concerned here.[12] Both tomb-chests exhibit two discrete horizontal layers, the narrow upper part of the third duke's monument consisting of plain moulded panels, whilst Richmond's features narrative reliefs, separated by herms (Figs 2 and 6). The complicated baluster shafts at the angles of the third duke's monument, visually linked by lions holding shields of Howard's heraldry to the tomb-chest, seem to be unique in the period (Figs 1–3). The Tudor Renaissance style of both monuments has been the subject of much study. The distinctive features of their architecture and sculpture are frequently cited as examples of French influence in England.[13] The religious imagery of the monuments is potentially of considerable importance for our understanding of the Tudor Renaissance and of the Reformation. Relief figures of the Apostles (and of two Old Testament figures) standing under shell niches, surround the tomb-chest of the third duke's monument. Old Testament narratives occupy the upper section of Richmond's tomb-chest, on top of which stand figures which are generally identified as angels (though they are wingless) holding coats of arms and instruments of Christ's Passion (Fig. 9).[14] Although only the most extreme Tudor evangelicals could find such imagery objectionable, sculpture of this kind became very uncommon in churches after the aggressively iconoclastic Reformation of Edward VI's reign (1547–53) and there was only very limited opportunity for a return to traditional iconography during the short duration of the Marian reaction (1553–8).[15] So, the subject matter of the imagery, as well as the monuments' style, make it extremely important to situate their date of production accurately within the mid-sixteenth century, a period of rapid and unpredictable changes of religious direction. Historians' interpretations of the monuments' meaning and evaluations of their significance will, naturally, change

[12] Another book from the 'Representing Re-Formation' team will discuss the other monuments at greater length.
[13] The two major earlier studies of the monuments are by L. Stone & H. M. Colvin, 'The Howard Tombs at Framlingham, Suffolk', *Archaeological Journal*, 122 (1965), 159–171 and R. Marks, 'The Howard Tombs at Thetford and Framlingham: New Discoveries', *Archaeological Journal*, 141 (1984), 252–68. The larger context is discussed in P. Lindley, 'Innovations, Tradition and Disruption in Tomb-sculpture', in D. Gaimster & P. Stamper (eds), *The Age of Transition: The Archaeology of English Culture 1400–1600*, Oxford 1997, 77–92.
[14] I have benefited from discussion of the figures with Dr James Bettley.
[15] P. Lindley, *Tomb Destruction and Scholarship: Medieval Monuments in Early Modern England*, Donington 2007, chs 1 and 3; P. Sherlock, *Monuments and Memory in Early Modern England*, Aldershot 2008, 132–3. Rebecca Constabel, in her PhD associated with the project, has noted the absence of tombs with images of saints between 1540 and 1590 in France.

depending on the date to which the tombs are assigned. For example, if the third duke's and Richmond's monuments should belong to Mary's reign, as has sometimes been argued, then they could be adduced as evidence for a nascent, if soon aborted, return to traditional religious imagery, commissioned by a religious conservative at the end of his life.[16]

The heraldry of the monuments has never received much attention from scholars, beyond its mere identification, but – as the treason charges against the Howards demonstrate – in the mid-sixteenth century, heraldry was not the esoteric, old-fashioned and irrelevant subject it appears to be to most modern viewers. On the contrary, it was one which possessed profound significance for the social and political elite, because it asserted lineage, heredity and status.[17] On Richmond's monument, coats of arms proclaiming his parentage and position alongside those of his Howard wife, are separately carved under projecting ducal coronets (Fig. 10) (the latter often now broken and in some cases cut back to the tomb chest). They dominate the main body of the tomb-chest. Heraldic shields and heraldic beasts are an even more prominent feature of the fourth duke's monument and are a feature of the small wall-tomb next to it, although the shields were never carved with heraldic identification on Elizabeth's tomb-chest. In fact, it is obvious that all four monuments are incomplete or unfinished, to varying degrees. We have already noted that there are no effigies on Richmond's memorial, and that the fourth duke's monument, which features effigies of his first two wives, lacks those of the duke and of his third wife, Elizabeth, whom he married in 1567. Two small figures are missing from each of the baluster shafts at the corners of the third duke's monument and other figures or features appear to be lost from above the half-shafts of the tomb-chest. It seems safe to deduce that the absence of such figures is not the result of iconoclasm motivated by religious ideology in the sixteenth or seventeenth centuries. For, not only does one figure still survive (facing inwards to the tomb-chest) on each shaft (Fig. 11), but the prominent survival of potentially more offensive religious imagery on the monuments proves that they escaped such attacks. A superstructure was probably intended for the fourth duke's tomb, judging by the substantial polygonal bases in place, but none was ever constructed. Nor was any of the monuments painted. Such painting normally took place only after the object was structurally complete and its absence is another important indication that the monuments were never finished. Before we can investigate these issues, though, we must first ask why the Howard

[16] The differences between the editors' views of the Marian Counter-Reformation in E. Duffy & D. Loades (eds), *The Church of Mary Tudor*, Aldershot 2006 become explicit when one compares E. Duffy, *Fires of Faith: Catholic England under Mary Tudor*, New Haven 2009 with D. Loades, *The Religious Culture of Marian England*, London 2010.

monuments are to be found in the parish church of St Michael, Framlingham in the first place.

Commissions, Abandonment and Salvage

The Howards were England's most powerful noble family under the Tudor monarchs. The political, military and religious events which decisively determined the future of the country, and in which many members of the family were critically important protagonists, influenced the formal and iconographic features of the Howards' monuments, the topography of their burial positions and even the choices of churches in which they were interred. Thetford Priory had been the burial place of the some of the Bigod earls of Norfolk (who had founded the priory at the beginning of the twelfth century) and subsequently of the Mowbray dukes.[18] The Cluniac priory was adopted by the Howards once they had been elevated to the vacant dukedom, after the death of John Mowbray in 1476 brought his line to an end. Sir Robert Howard had married Margaret (d. 1459), daughter of Duke Thomas Mowbray (d. 1399), and Robert's son, Sir John, was one of two legal co-heirs, through his mother. Richard III bestowed the dukedom on John two days after his successful usurpation of the throne in 1483, as a reward for his support. John, the first Howard duke, was killed loyally fighting for Richard at the Battle of Bosworth, but his son, Thomas, who had fought alongside his father, now changed his allegiance. Bosworth, a catastrophe for the Catesbys, was merely a setback for the Howards.[19] Thomas Howard was formally pardoned in 1486 but he was not elevated to the dukedom until 1514, after his decisive defeat of the Scots at Flodden Field had unequivocally demonstrated his loyalty to the young Henry VIII.

By selecting Thetford as their own burial place, the Howard dukes explicitly asserted their continuity with their famous predecessors, just as the Despensers, for example, had chosen burial at Tewkesbury alongside the abbey's Norman founder, Robert Fitz-Hamon, and the Despensers' glamorous Clare predecessors.[20] The Howards' earlier burial locations had been at East Winch in

[17]   See P. Lindley, 'The Poetics of the Tudor Beast', in M. Stocker and P. Lindley (eds) *Tributes to Jean Michel Massing: Towards a Global History of Art*, Turnhout 2015 (forthcoming).

[18]   E.g. Earl Roger, d. 1270. See also J. Weever, *Ancient Funerall Monuments*, London 1631, 829. Roger Bigod had wished to be buried in the church, but his body was seized by the bishop and interred in Norwich Cathedral. See Dr Hall's essay, above.

[19]   S. Payling, '"Never desire to be great about princes, for it is daungeros": the rise and fall of the fifteenth-century Catesbys', in J. Bertram (ed.) *The Catesby Family and their Brasses at Ashby St Ledgers*, London 2006, 1–17.

[20]   P. Lindley, 'The Later Medieval Monuments and Chantry Chapels', in R. K. Morris & R. Shoesmith (eds) *Tewkesbury Abbey: History, Art & Architecture*, Logaston 2003, 161–82.

Norfolk, and in the fifteenth century, Stoke-by-Nayland in Suffolk, the centre of Lord John Howard's estates before his elevation to the dukedom and inheritance of Mowbray lands in East Anglia.[21] The west tower of the fine church at Stoke-by-Nayland prominently displays the arms of an earlier Sir John Howard (d. 1400) and his wife, the heiress Alice Tendring (d. 1426), and later Howards were major contributors to the rebuilding of the church. The south chapel still contains the brass of Duke John's first wife, Catherine, *née* Moleyns.[22] Although she died in the mid-fifteenth century, the brass was commissioned in the 1530s as a retrospective monument to enhance the family's dignity (Fig. 12).[23] Duke John was therefore separated both from his Howard ancestors and from his immediate family when he was interred at Thetford Priory in 1485 on the south side of the nave.[24] The decision was doubtless taken by his son, Duke Thomas. Duke John's second wife, Margaret Chedworth, who post-deceased him, dying in 1494, was interred at Stoke-by-Nayland, as his first wife had been.[25]

In his seventies (he was born in 1443), Thomas, the second Howard duke (d. 1524), chose Thetford as his own burial site, selecting the most prestigious position, in front of the high altar.[26] He commissioned the celebrated East Anglian master mason John Wastell as its designer, as his will of 31 May 1520 (proved on 16 July 1524) reveals:[27]

> We woll that our said Executors cause our tombe to be made and sett in the said Church of the priory of Thetford directly before the high awter where it was devised by us, Maister Clerk (sic. for Larke) maister of the King's workis at Cambridge and Wastell fremason of Bury in the Countie

21 Sir Robert Howard (d. 1389) and his wife were buried in East Winch (Marks, 265). Sir John had been promoted to the baronage by Edward IV.

22 Weever, 774–5. Marks, 253 & 254 and pl. VIIIa, states that Catherine died in 1452 (citing the now lost inscription depicted by Weever and Lilly), as does R. Green, *The History, Topography, and Antiquities, of Framlingham and Saxsted*, London 1834, 65, but the correct date is 1465. D. MacCulloch (ed.), *The Chorography of Suffolk, Suffolk Records Society, XIX (1976)*, 85, has 1456.

23 Marks, 254. The indents of the lost brasses of Duke John's grandparents – John Howard and Alice Tendring, through whom the estate came to the Howards – still exist nearby. Weever, 773, shows the indent with inscription and two coats of arms still extant. The couple were also depicted in the stained glass of the church's east window, depicted in Weever, 772. The future third duke had lived at Stoke while his father resided at Framlingham.

24 Marks, 254, cites TNA SP1/227 f.128.

25 For Duchess Margaret's tomb, MacCulloch, *Chorography*, 86 and n. 132.

26 T. Woodcock and J. M. Robinson, *The Oxford Guide to Heraldry*, Oxford 1988, 178–9 describe his funeral ceremonies as the last great funeral of the Middle Ages.

27 Stone & Colvin, 162. The will recites an indenture of 31 August 1516 *pace* J. H. Harvey, *English Medieval Architects*, Gloucester 1984, 323.

of Norffolk. And the pictours of us and Agnes our wife to be sett togider thereuppon.[28]

Thomas Larke was one of Wolsey's protégés, and the brother of the cardinal's mistress; as well as surveyor of works at King's College, Cambridge, he was also archdeacon of Sudbury and of Norwich and Master of Trinity Hall.[29] John Wastell was the master mason responsible for the structural completion of King's College Chapel. Wastell seems to have deceased in May 1515 and was certainly dead by May 1518, so he cannot have been the tomb's executant, though he presumably provided a design.[30]

An enormously lengthy text panel, providing a detailed resumé of the duke's career, was transcribed from a copy of the original by the great seventeenth-century antiquary John Weever, who says the panel had been fixed to the tomb-monument.[31] The text began by stating that an epitaph around the tomb gave the duke's ancestry 'wyche is also set out in armes about the same tombe', indicating that the tomb-chest was studded with heraldic shields. The monument thus exemplifies the point that heraldic self-identification, proclaiming ancestry and family marital alliances, was a prevalent concern of the nobility in this period, with their potent belief in the innate superiority of ancient families and the transmission of honour through blood. The duke was also Earl Marshal, with jurisdiction over the College of Arms, according him a pre-eminent position at this critical period in the development of the college's authority from recording heraldry to regulating it. The prestigious office was very important to the third duke too. He clashed with Wolsey when the cardinal secured the office's reversion, on the second duke's death, to the duke of Suffolk and regained the post in 1533.[32] The third duke's personal pride and interest in his own ancestry and status seems to have been particularly fervent. In 1532, he sought (and obtained) permission from the Venetian signoria for the repatriation of the bones of his maternal great-grandfather, Thomas Mowbray, first duke of Norfolk, who had died in Venice in 1399, whilst exiled from the court of Richard II, for reinterment in England.[33] It was presumably around this time that he

28 PCC 23 Bodfield [now catalogued as PROB 11/21/391 according to Kirsten Claiden-Yardley to whom I am grateful for the information] cited by Stone & Colvin, 162, n. 16.
29 H. M. Colvin (ed.), *History of the King's Works*, III/1, 189, n. 2. His family may have originated in Thetford.
30 Harvey, *EMA*, 325 doubts that the John Wastell of Bury who died in 1515/16 was the master mason.
31 Weever, 833–40. Lancaster herald, Nicholas Charles, writing in 1611, twenty years before Weever's publication, describes it as hanging by the monument (Marks, 255).
32 *ODNB* s.n.
33 *Calendar of State Papers and Manuscripts ... existing in the Archives and Collections of Venice*, IV, *1527–1533*, ed. Rawdon Brown, London 1871, nos 837, 857. In

commissioned the retrospective brass for his grandmother at Stoke-by-Nayland, with her heraldic surcoat and coats of arms set into the matrix.

The second duke's tomb has been lost, for reasons which will be set out shortly, but its appearance is known from a drawing by Sir Thomas Writhe (he 'improved' his name to Wriothesley) (d. 1534), Garter King of Arms (Fig. 13).[34] Sir Thomas's nephew, Lord Chancellor Thomas Wriothesley KG (1505–50), later first earl of Southampton – played important roles in the examinations and convictions of both Lord Thomas Howard (d. 1537), second son of the second duke's second marriage (to Agnes *née* Tilney) and of Henry VIII's fifth wife, Queen Catherine Howard (daughter of Edmund, third surviving son of the second duke's first marriage), in 1541. He was also, as we have seen, deeply involved in the destruction of Surrey and in the attempted destruction of the third duke, so the drawing also has a secondary, rather sinister, interest.[35] The second duke's monument is shown to have been freestanding, with a tomb-chest displaying twelve heraldic shields housed under Gothic trefoiled arches, bearing a recumbent effigy of the duke. The inscription is not indicated on the drawing. Contrary to the duke's instructions to his executors, there was no representation of his wife on the monument. In fact, by the time that she drew up her own will in 1542, Duchess Agnes had decided on burial at Lambeth, ordering: 'My bodye to be buried within the parish churche of Lambithe Co. Surrey in suche place whereas I have prepared my Tombe'.[36] In 1522, Duke Thomas had built a family chapel in the north aisle at Lambeth which once housed a series of epitaphs to various members of the Howard family.[37] The church was close to his great residence, Norfolk House, which he used as his main suburban house when in the capital.[38] From the text of Duchess Agnes Howard's will, it seems certain

---

February 1533 they were unable to find the duke's burial place. The reason for this may be that he was buried in St George's abbey, Venice (pace *GEC*), but the 3rd Duke had informed them that Mowbray was buried in St Mark's.

[34] British Library, Additional MS 45131, f. 85 – first identified by Richard Marks and Ann Payne – by Thomas Wriothesley, Garter King of Arms (see Marks, 256, for details of heraldry) For Wriothesley, see Robert Yorke's entry in *ODNB*.

[35] For Lord Chancellor Wriothesley, *ODNB*, entry by Michael A. R. Graves. He became Earl of Southampton in 1547. He and the 3rd duke had together participated in the humiliation of Thomas Cromwell on 10 June 1540.

[36] Marks, 257, cites it from G. Leveson-Gower, 'The Howards of Effingham', *Surrey Archaeological Collections*, IX (1888), 395–436 (427); PCC 40 Pynnyng, cited by Stone & Colvin, 161 n.10 and see also 162.

[37] Stone & Colvin, 160, were uncertain whether these monuments were removed from Stoke and Thetford at a later date or whether they recorded original burials. They cite O. Manning and W. Bray, *History of Surrey*, London 1814, III, 504–6.

[38] H. Roberts and W. H. Godfrey (eds), *Survey of London, 23, Lambeth, South Bank and Vauxhall*, London 1951, 137–40.

that her tomb-monument had been constructed by March 1542 and although, oddly, she is sometimes said to have been initially interred at Thetford on 31 May 1545, it is clear that she was buried at Lambeth on 13 October of the same year.[39] Like her husband's tomb-monument, that of duchess Agnes has been destroyed, but its appearance is known from a drawing, this time a seventeenth-century one, by Henry Lilly, Rougedragon Pursuivant (d. 1638), in his pedigree of the Howards now preserved at Arundel Castle.[40] By the time that Lilly drew it, that is to say before the period of systematic Commonwealth iconoclasm, it had already lost its inscription and the arms on the sides and ends were defaced.[41] The tomb-chest was a relatively plain Purbeck marble object, the brass a representation of the Duchess in her heraldic vestments, under a triple canopy supported by pinnacles each adorned with three coats of arms. Professor Marks has indicated that it resembled the monument of Katharine Howard (*née* Broughton) (d. 1535) which still exists at Lambeth.[42]

Other members of the Howard family had also been buried at Thetford in the early sixteenth century. The Priory's register mentions the grave of Duchess Anne (d. 1511), daughter of Edward IV and the first wife of Thomas, later the third duke.[43] It also includes a reference to the gravestone of Lord Thomas Howard, son of the second duke and his second wife, Duchess Agnes, who, as mentioned above, was attainted in 1536 for aspiring to marry the king's niece (Lady Margaret Douglas). He died in the Tower of London on 31 October 1537 and was buried at Thetford.[44] In 1536, the third duke's son-in-law, Henry Fitzroy, duke of Richmond & Somerset, Henry VIII's bastard son by Elizabeth Blount, was also buried there.[45] The third duke himself intended to be buried in the priory church and had commissioned monuments for himself and for his

---

[39]   D. Dymond (ed.), *The Register of Thetford Priory*, 2 vols, Norfolk Record Society, 59 & 60 (1995–6), I, 60 n. 191. See also *ODNB* entry by Catharine Davies. Leveson-Gower, 397–8 disputes the fact that she was buried at Thetford and I can find no evidence for it. The Lambeth Parish Register records her burial on 13 October.

[40]   C. R. Manning, 'Brasses of Thomas Howard, Second Duke of Nofolk, and Agnes his wife (1524)', *Norfolk Archaeology*, VIII (1877), 40–50. See *ODNB* entry by Thomas Woodcock. It was later in the possession of Mary Compton [*née* Noel] Countess of Northampton *GEC*, 682, n. h.

[41]   Marks, 257.

[42]   Ibid. and pls. XI a and b.

[43]   Dymond (ed.), *Register*, I, 37–8. Dymond's work supersedes J. H. Harvey, 'The Last Years of Thetford Priory', *Norfolk Archaeology*, 27 (1941), 1–28.

[44]   Dymond (ed.), *Register*, I, 38, n. 103 notes that Marks, 261, wrongly takes the reference on f. 274v of the Thetford Register to apply to the tomb of Thomas, the third duke. The reference, Dymond (ed.), *Register*, II, 695, is 'Eodem (Johanni Swhett) pro le laying of a graveston' pro Domino Thome Howard 6d'. For Lord Thomas, see *ODNB* entry by Michael Riordan.

[45]   Dymond (ed.), *Register*, II, 665. See also *L&P*, XI (1536), nos. 233, 236.

son-in-law by 1539.[46] We know this because the duke told the king about them, when he was trying to save the priory from dissolution that year:

> thentent of the saide Duke is, that if it may stande with his highnes pleasure that he may so have it, to make a parisshe Churche of the same, wher nowe doth lye buried the bodie of the late Duke of Richemond the kings naturall sonn, and also the bodie of the late [first] wiff of the said Duke, the lady Anne awnte to his highnes, the bodie of the late Duke of Norffolk father to the said Duke, and also the bodies of diverse other Dukes, and other auncestours to the saide Duke, and also doth entende to lye their hymself, *havyng alrady made twoo Tombes, one for the saide Duke of Richemond and an other for hymself, whiche have alredy and woll cost hym, or they can be fully set uppe & fynisshed, iiij^c li. at the least.*[47]

In spite of the duke's efforts – after his earlier proposal that the priory should be converted into a secular college was rejected, he had suggested that the church could become a 'very honest' parish church – the priory was dissolved on 16 February 1540, and the priory and all its possessions were surrendered to the crown.[48] The third duke was nevertheless permitted to buy the site and all the priory estates the same year: with other pickings from Coxford and Castle Acre priories, monastic dissolutions had enabled him to double his possessions in the county.[49]

Unfortunately, we do not know exactly what happened to the priory buildings in the next few years: usually valuable materials were quickly removed from dissolved churches, and in the case of lead from the roofs, melted down and sent to London.[50] The commissioners' instructions were to pull down the walls of the ecclesiastical buildings of dissolved houses. Here, some of the domestic buildings certainly remained habitable: the former prior remained in his fine lodgings and the lawyer Stephen Draper lived somewhere else in the monastery.[51]

---

[46]   Richmond married Mary, the third duke's younger daughter by his second wife, Elizabeth Stafford. See *ODNB* entry by Beverley A. Murphy.

[47]   Stone & Colvin, 160, citing PRO [TNA] SP 1/156, f.115 My emphasis. *L&P*, XIV/2 (1539), no. 815. Dymond (ed.) *Register*, I, 56 suggests that the Duke's petition to convert the priory church into a parish church (*L&P*, XIV/2 (1539), no. 816) may date from as early as 1536, but this seems unlikely. For the prior's visit to London in 1538/9 probably in connection with the proposed conversion of the priory into a secular college, Dymond (ed.) *Register*, II, 706.

[48]   Dymond (ed.), *Register*, I, 56–8; the deed of surrender is illustrated II, facing title page. For the proposal that it should become a college, see *L&P*, XIV/2 (1539), nos. 430 and 816. For the surrender, see *L&P HVIII*, XV (1540) no. 211. For Howard's unscrupulous earlier dealings with other monastic houses, MacCulloch, *Suffolk*, 66.

[49]   For the grant to Norfolk, *L&P*, XV (1540), 942 (43); Dymond (ed.), *Register*, I, 59.

[50]   D. Knowles, *The Religious Orders in England, III, The Tudor Age*, Cambridge 1971, ch. xxx.

[51]   Dymond (ed.), *Register*, I, 59, n. 180. and ibid., 65–6 that the prior's lodging survived

The church was still standing, with tomb monuments inside, when those sent from court investigated its heraldry, presumably still in December 1546, during the attack on the Howards.[52] Dr Moore has shown that there was no herald amongst those sent to investigate the heraldry, so the case against Surrey and his father must have been contrived as he has convincingly argued, 'following the collapse of more serious charges'.[53] Chancellor Wriothesley prepared a list of nine charges which Henry VIII himself reviewed and annotated. The king's angry judgments were, of course, decisive. The first charge accused Norfolk of placing the arms of Thomas of Brotherton in the wrong quarter of his shield and of using the wrong label of difference on those arms. However, the system of marks of difference on which the duke's accusers rested their case, and which had been invented by Wriothesley's grandfather, had never been fully adopted: the case was absurd. Surrey was also accused of claiming the arms of Edward the Confessor.[54] In fact, Surrey was fully entitled to use these arms, which Richard II had granted to Thomas Mowbray, first duke of Norfolk and he himself cited examples in the priory church at Thetford; but he was certainly insensitive to warnings about the message conveyed by his display of them and his belief that his right to bear them antedated the Norman Conquest was false.[55] Whatever implausible convolutions and internal contradictions are revealed in the tainted evidence against the Howards, one thing is certain: Surrey's heraldry, because of the claims to inheritance and blood-lines it indicated and symbolized, was viewed by the king as treasonous. What also seems clear is that no monument to the third duke was then present in the priory church at Thetford: otherwise, its existence would certainly have been noted and its heraldry recorded. We can be equally certain that no monument to Richmond was visible. In her essay below, Kirsten Claiden-Yardley deduces that two monuments which were described by the men investigating the heraldry were Mowbray tombs, probably commemorating the third (d. 1461) and fourth Mowbray dukes (d. 1476). She also argues that the reason that the second Howard duke's monument was not mentioned is that it was no longer in the centre of the choir. An explanation can be offered why this should have been the case.

The precise evolution of the third duke's plans for his and Richmond's monuments between the dissolution of Thetford Priory and his fall in December 1546 is unclear. As we have noted above, his step-mother's decision to be buried

as a house till 1737.
[52] Moore, 'Heraldic Charge,' 560.
[53] Moore, 'Heraldic Charge,' 559.
[54] Moore, 'Heraldic Charge,' 563, n. 1. *L&P*, XXI/2 (1546–7), no. 555.14; *GEC*, 603. n. b.
[55] Moore, 'Heraldic Charge,' 563. I differ from Dr Moore in believing that Surrey meant Thetford, not East Winch when he cited 'the church in Norfolk'.

1 (Hall).
Aerial view
of the priory,
looking north
(© English
Heritage).

2 (Hall). Prior's Lodging, looking north-east; note re-used Romanesque arches in the centre of the building. The building stands west of the church, facing the gatehouse to the north (Tom Arber).

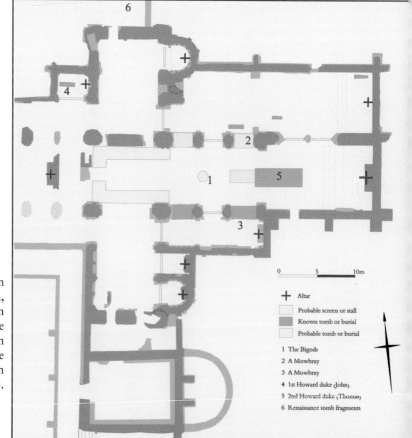

3 (Hall). Eastern arm of church, showing known and probable tomb and screen locations (Jackie Hall using English Heritage plan).

0   5   10m

+ Altar

Probable screen or stall

Known tomb or burial

Probable tomb or burial

1 The Bigods
2 A Mowbray
3 A Mowbray
4 1st Howard duke (John)
5 2nd Howard duke (Thomas)
6 Renaissance tomb fragments

4 (Hall). Fragment of painted and gilded cornice from a late medieval screen, 11.6cm wide (Jackie Hall).

5 (Hall). Tympanum, with lion (c.35cm wide) – one of many fine Romanesque sculptured and rchitectural pieces surviving from the early priory (© Norwich Castle Museum and Art Gallery).

6 (Hall). The church, looking east, with the nave altar in the foreground and the high altar, raised on steps, in the middle distance (Tom Arber).

7 (Hall). Horse harness, c.3cm wide (Jackie Hall).

8 (Hall). Pilgrim badge (c.4.7cm high), late 15th-century, with an annunciation scene (Jackie Hall).

Hall). Fragment of delicate Perpendicular screen-work, c.13.5cm high (Jackie Hall).

10 (Hall). Hollow spiral shaft (outer diameter, c.5.8cm), part of an ornate and original composition, perhaps around or on top of a tomb (Jackie Hall).

(Hall). Bunch of grapes (c.5cm high) from p of a hollow spiral shaft carved as a vine (Jackie Hall).

12 (Hall). Fragment of painted wall plaster (c.6cm wide), indicative of the brightly coloured interior that once existed (Jackie Hall).

13 (Hall). Fragment of plaster cornice (*c.*22.5cm wide), just possibly from a tomb or tomb canopy. Smaller matching fragments retained gilding on their surface. (Jackie Hall).

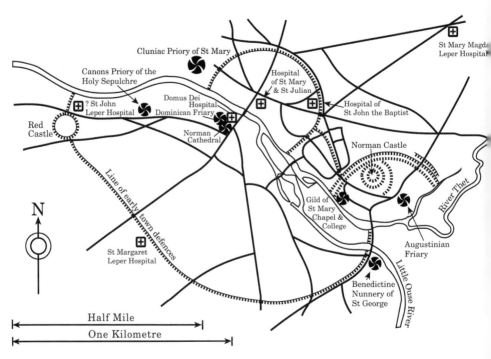

14 (Hall). Map showing the location of the medieval religious houses of Thetford (© Sue White).

15 (Hall). Late 17th-century view of the priory ruins, looking south-east, by Wenceslas Hollar © The Pepys Library, Magdalene College, Cambridge).

16 (Hall). Late-eighteenth-century print of the priory ruins, looking north-west (NMAS: Ancient House, Thetford).

THE OLD ABBEY RUINS,
THETFORD.

17 (Hall). Postcard of the priory ruins, c.1910, looking north-east
(NMAS: Ancient House, Thetford).

18 (Hall). Rare photograph of the early clearance excavations, looking east from the crossing,
taken on 17th September 1934 (NMAS: Ancient House, Thetford).

(Lindley). Tomb monument of Thomas, the third Howard Duke of Norfolk (d. 1554), and his first wife, Anne (d. 1511), daughter of Edward IV, from the south-west (Paul Bryan, English Heritage).

2 (Lindley) The same monument, south side (Phillip Lindley).

3 (Lindley, overleaf). The same monument, north side. (Phillip Lindley).

This Isle is repaired by
PEMBROKE-HALL
FRAMLINGHAM
COGGESHALL
and DEBENHAM

4 (Lindley). Tomb monument of Henry Fitzroy, Duke of Richmond & Somerset (d. 1536) and his wife Duchess Mary [Howard] (d. 1555), from the north west (Paul Bryan, English Heritage).
5 (Lindley). The same tomb from the south west (Phillip Lindley).

6 (Lindley). Tomb monument of Henry Fitzroy, Duke of Richmond & Somerset (d. 1536) and his wife Duchess Mary [Howard] (d. 1555), south side (Phillip Lindley).

7 (Lindley). Tomb monument of Duchesses Mary Fitzalan (d. 25 August 1557) and Margaret Audley (d. 10 January 1564), the first two of the three wives of Thomas Howard, the fourth duke (d. 1572), from the south west (Phillip Lindley).

8 (Lindley).Tomb monument of the fourth duke's daughter, Elizabeth Howard (d.c. 1565),
from the south (Phillip Lindley).

(Lindley). Wingless figure holding coat of arms and instruments of Christ's Passion, m Richmond's monument (Phillip Lindley).

11 (Lindley). Old Testament prophet with scroll, on baluster shaft, third duke's monument (Phillip Lindley).

(Lindley). Carved ducal coronet above coat of arms, Richmond's monument (Phillip Lindley).

13 (Lindley). Tomb monument of Thomas Howard, second Duke of Norfolk, depicted by
Sir Thomas Wriothesley), Garter King of Arms, British Library, Additional MS 45131, f. 85
(© Copyright The British Library Board).

(Lindley, opposite)). Retrospective brass of Catherine Howard,
ɔke-by-Nayland, Suffolk (Phillip Lindley).

14 (Lindley). Motte, Thetford Castle (Phillip Lindley).

15 (Lindley). Framlingham Castle (Phillip Lindley).

16 (Lindley). East end of chancel, St Michael's, Framlingham, Suffolk (Phillip Lindley).

17 (Lindley). South aisle of chancel, St Michael's, Framlingham, Suffolk (Phillip Lindley).

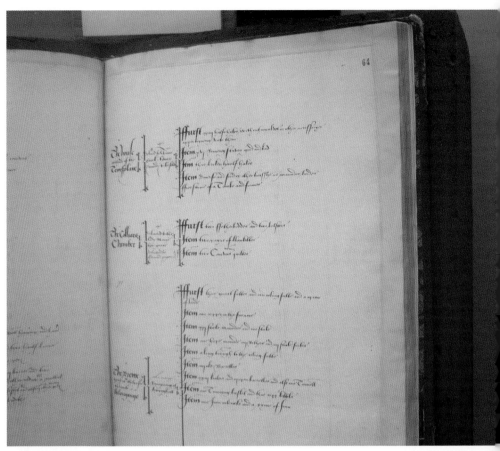

18 (Lindley). TNA, LR2/115 (the 1551 version of the inventory), folio 64r (Kate Adcock).

19 (Lindley). Mason's marks, on Richmond monument, also found on the third duke's monume
(Phillip Lindley).

20 (Lindley). 1555 graffito on Richmond's monument (Phillip Lindley).

21 (Lindley). Detail of the effigy of the third duke (Phillip Lindley).

22 (Lindley). Detail of the effigy of the duchess (Phillip Lindley).

23 (Lindley). Three components of a detached shaft, excavated on the site of Thetford Priory in the 1930s (Phillip Lindley).

24 (Lindley). Three components (of 4) of a half-shaft, excavated on the site of Thetford Priory in the 1930s (Phillip Lindley).

25 (Lindley, below, left). Kneeling angel with arms of Christ's Passion (3 nails) excavated on the site of Thetford Priory in the 1930s (Phillip Lindley).

26 (Lindley). Kneeling angel with arms of Christ's Passion (crown of thorns) excavated on the site of Thetford Priory in the 1930s (Phillip Lindley).

27 (Lindley). Angel with the three Magi relief, excavated on the site of Thetford Priory in the 1930s (Phillip Lindley).

28 (Lindley). Fragment of sabaton excavated on the site of Thetford Priory in the 1930s (Phillip Lindley).

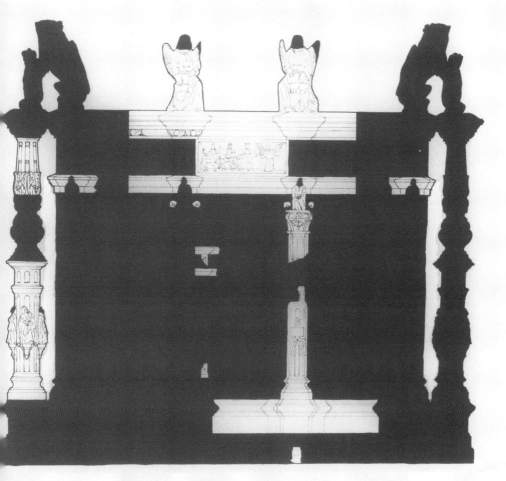

END ELEVATION OF TOMB
SHOWING CONJECTURED POSITION
OF REMAINING FRAGMENTS

SCALE · OF · FEET

JANUARY
1936

375
10

29 (Lindley). G. H. Chettle's 1936 hypothesized reconstruction of the monument incorporating the excavated fragments.

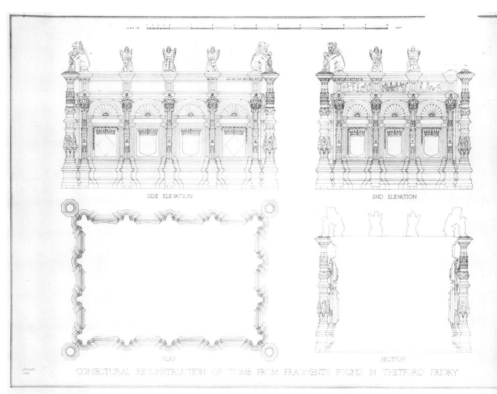

30 (Lindley). G. H. Chettle, hypothesized reconstruction of the whole monument incorporating the excavated fragments.

31 (Lindley). Old Testament prophet bust-length relief, excavated on the site of Thetford Prior in the nineteenth century (Phillip Lindley).

2 (Lindley). Old Testament king bust-length relief, excavated on the site of Thetford Priory in the nineteenth century (Phillip Lindley).

33 (Lindley). Fragment of Old Testament figure, excavated on the site of Thetford Priory in the 1930s (Phillip Lindley).

34 (Lindley). Detail of Drunkeness of Noah relief, from Richmond's monument, showing flint inclusion (Phillip Lindley).

35 (Lindley). Triangular-shaped repair to Apostle relief from third duke's monument (Phillip Lindley).

36 (Lindley). Detail of St John the Evangelist figure, from the east end of the third duke's monument (Phillip Lindley).

37 (Lindley). Europac laser scanning monuments of the fourth duke and Elizabeth Howard, Framlingham (Phillip Lindley).

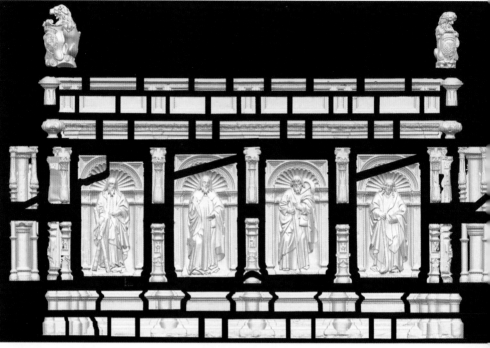

38 (Lindley). Nishad Karim's virtual disassembly of south side of the third duke's monument, based on 3D scans and Lindley and Atherton's identification of individual stones of the monument. Effigies omitted.

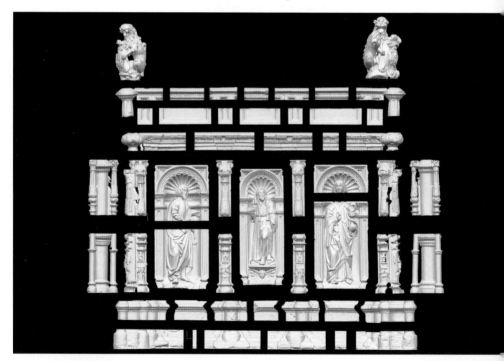

39 (Lindley). Nishad Karim's virtual disassembly of east end of the third duke's monument, based on 3D scans and Lindley and Atherton's identification of individual stones of the monument. Effigies omitted.

40 (Lindley). Europac scanning British Museum panel (Phillip Lindley).

41 (Lindley). Painted figure wrongly assigned to the components of the third duke's and Richmond's monuments, showing that it is too large to fit where Chettle had placed it in his reconstruction.

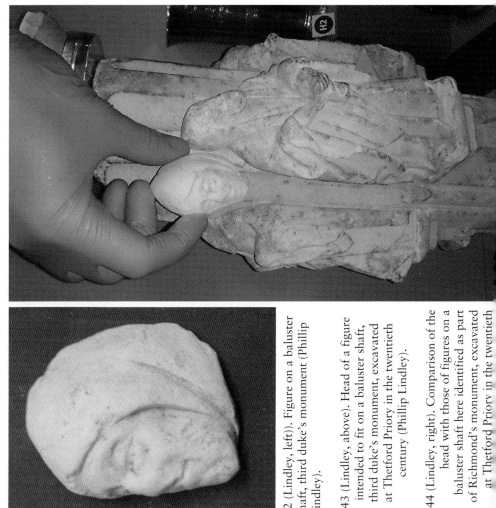

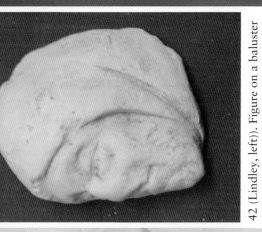

42 (Lindley, left). Figure on a baluster shaft, third duke's monument (Phillip Lindley).

43 (Lindley, above). Head of a figure intended to fit on a baluster shaft, third duke's monument, excavated at Thetford Priory in the twentieth century (Phillip Lindley).

44 (Lindley, right). Comparison of the head with those of figures on a baluster shaft here identified as part of Richmond's monument, excavated at Thetford Priory in the twentieth

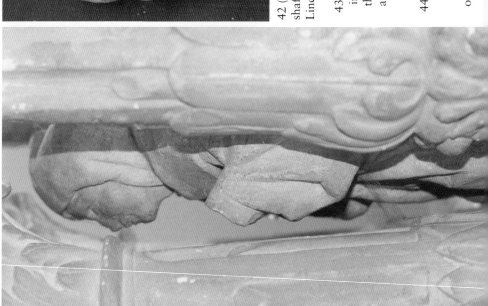

The *tomb-monuments* of Thomas Howard, 3rd Duke of Norfolk (d.1554) and of Henry Duke of Richmond and Somerset (d.1536), St Michael's, Framlingham, Suffolk.

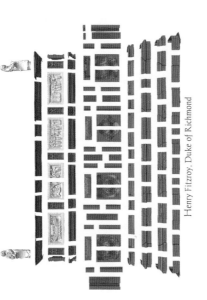

Henry Fitzroy, Duke of Richmond

Key

☐ Stone
Phase 1, c. 1539, Carved in Thetford, when the monuments were planned to stand in Thetford Priory Church.

■ Red
Phase 2, 1550s, Carved in Framlingham, when the monuments were hurriedly finished and set up.

■ Blue
Heraldic Lion, moved from the 4th Duke's monument.

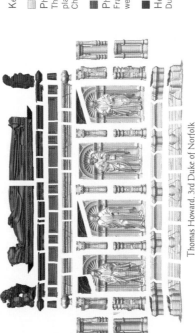

Thomas Howard, 3rd Duke of Norfolk

45 (Lindley). Disassembly of the monuments showing phasing of components (Ian Drake and Nishad Karim following Lindley and Atherton).

46 (Lindley). Incised numbering marks on top surface of British Museum Old Testament relief panel (Phillip Lindley).

47 (Lindley). Incised number on top surface of Three Magi and angel panel [shown in Lindley Fig. 27] (Phillip Lindley).

8 (Lindley). Nishad Karim's conjectural reconstruction of one bay of the third duke's monument as originally planned, with Magi relief incorporated to scale.

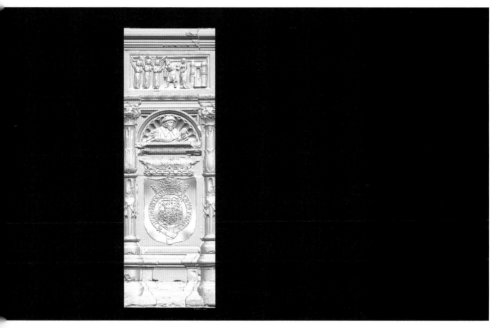

9 (Lindley). Nishad Karim's conjectural reconstruction of one bay of Richmond's monument as originally planned, with BM panel, half shaft and base elements incorporated, to scale.

(Lindley, opposite). Creation of Eve,
hmond's monument,
mlingham (Phillip Lindley).

1 (Constabel). Framlingham, third Howard duke of Norfolk's tomb (Rebecca Constabel).

2 (Constabel). Tomb of François II and Marguerite de Foix, Nantes (Rebecca Constabel).

3 (Constabel). Tomb of the dukes of Orleans, St Denis (Rebecca Constabel).

4 (Constabel, overleaf). Tomb of Artus Gouffier, Oiron (Rebecca Constabel).

and followed by 5 (Constabel). Tomb of Imbert de Batarnay, Montrésor (Rebecca Constabel).

6 (Constabel). Map of Norfolk's route.

7 (Constabel). 1559 date inscribed on the Howard tomb (Phillip Lindley).

8 (Constabel). 1555 date inscribed on Richmond's Tomb (Rebecca Constabel).

9 (Constabel). Graffito on Howard Tomb, south side (Phillip Lindley).

11 (Constabel). Detail, showing Antonio della Porta inscription
below the feet of the effigy (Rebecca Constabel).

(Constabel, opposite). Tomb of Raoul de Lannoy (d. 1508)
d Jehanne de Poix, Folleville (Rebecca Constabel).

12 (Constabel). Detail of inscription on the tomb of Artus Gouffier (Rebecca Constabel).

13 (Constabel). Bishop Thomas James's tomb, Dol-de-Bretagne: detail of Gothic inscription (Rebecca Constabel).

14 (Constabel, opposite). General view of Bishop Thomas James's tom
Dol-de-Bretagne (Rebecca Constab

1 (Fraser & Karim). Mason's individual mark, at centre of image, illustrating sub-mm resolution of laser-scanned virtual tomb.

2 (Fraser & Karim). Laser-scanned image of the east end or 'hidden face' of the third Duke's tomb. The height of the tomb to the level of the top plinth is approximately 1.6m. The effigies of the Duke and his wife are not shown.

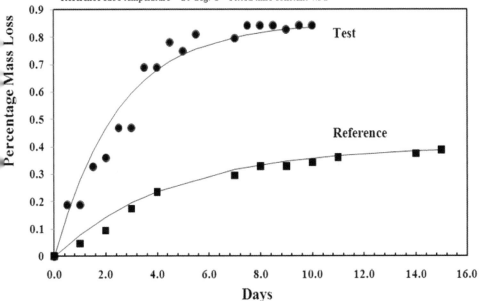

Air-bake of ABS *plus* thermoplastic cubes

Reference and Test cube volumes = 6 x 6 x 6 cm³.
Test cube temperature = 70 (Days 0-3), 100 deg.C   Fitted time constant 2.5d
Reference cube temperature = 20 deg. C   Fitted time constant 4.5d

3 (Fraser & Karim). Measurements of the mass loss from small blocks of one common material used in additive manufacture.

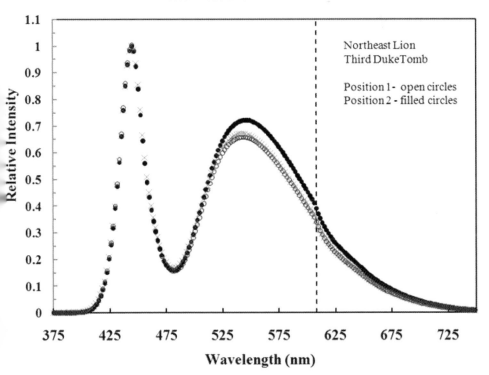

4 (Fraser & Karim). Optical reflectance spectroscopy results.

HENRICO H
NORFOLCIÆ
PATRI COMIT
EQVITI AV
MDXLVI A
EIVS FILIÆ IC
HOWARDVS
SECVNDO·
IN PARENT

IÆ SECVNDI DVCIS
NITO THOMÆ TERTII
GEORGIANI ORDINIS
RE ANNO SALVTIS
RANCISCÆ VXORI
OXONIÆ, HENRICVS
AMPTONIÆ FILIVS
VPREMVM PIETATIS
TVM POSVIT
1614.

In Dover Castle Church.

In the South part of the castle The church Monuments in the memories of the Earl of Northampton.

3 (Ford). Tomb of Henry Howard, Earl of Northampton, c. 1638, from Henry Lilly MS, G 1/1(
f. 130 Arundel Castle Archives. By kind permission of His Grace the Duke of Norfolk.

1 (Ford, previous pages). Tomb of Henry Howard, Earl of Surrey, and his wife,
Frances de Vere. The Church of St. Michael, Framlingham, Suffolk (Lisa Ford).

and 2 (Ford). Figures of Thomas Howard, fourth Duke of Norfolk, left, and
Henry Howard, Earl of Northampton, right, from the tomb of Henry Howard,
Earl of Surrey. The Church of St. Michael, Framlingham, Suffolk (Lisa Ford).

4 (Ford). Tomb of Ambrose Dudley, Earl of Warwick. Beauchamp Chapel,
The Collegiate Church of St. Mary, Warwick (Lisa Ford).

5 (Ford). Tomb of William Bourchier, third Earl of Bath, and his wife, Elizabeth Russell.
The Church of St. Peter, Tawstock, Devon (Lisa Ford).

6 (Ford). Inscription stone from the tomb of Henry Howard, Earl of Surrey. The Church of St. Michael, Framlingham, Suffolk (Lisa Ford).

HENRICO HOWARDO THOMÆ SECVNDI DVCIS NORFOLCIÆ FILIO PRIMOGENITO THOMÆ TERTII PATRI COMITI SVRRIÆ, ET GEORGIANI ORDINIS EQVITI AVRATO, IMMATVRE ANNO SALVTIS MDXLVI ABREPTO, ET FRANCISCÆ VXORI EIVS FILIÆ IOANNIS COMITIS OXONIÆ, HENRICVS HOWARDVS COMES NORTHAMPTONIÆ FILIVS SECVNDO-GENITVS HOC SVPREMVM PIETATIS IN PARENTES MONVMENTVM POSVIT ANNO DOMINI 1614.

7 (Ford). Inscription stone from the tomb of Henry Howard, Earl of Northampton. Trinity Hospital Greenwich, London (Lisa Ford).

IOHANNE GRIFFITHO HVIC COMITI AB EPISTOLIS CVRANTE

POSITVM

8 (Ford). Inscription stone from the tomb of Henry Howard, Earl of Surrey. The Church of St. Michael, Framlingham, Suffolk (Lisa Ford).

IOHANNE GRIFFITHO NVPER COMITI

9 (Ford). Photo taken during restoration of Surrey tomb at The Church of St. Michael, Framlingham, c. 1976. Archive of The Church of St. Michael, Framlingham.

10 (Ford). Coronet presently on tomb of Henry Howard, Earl of Surrey, The Church of St. Michael, Framlingham, Suffolk (Lisa Ford).

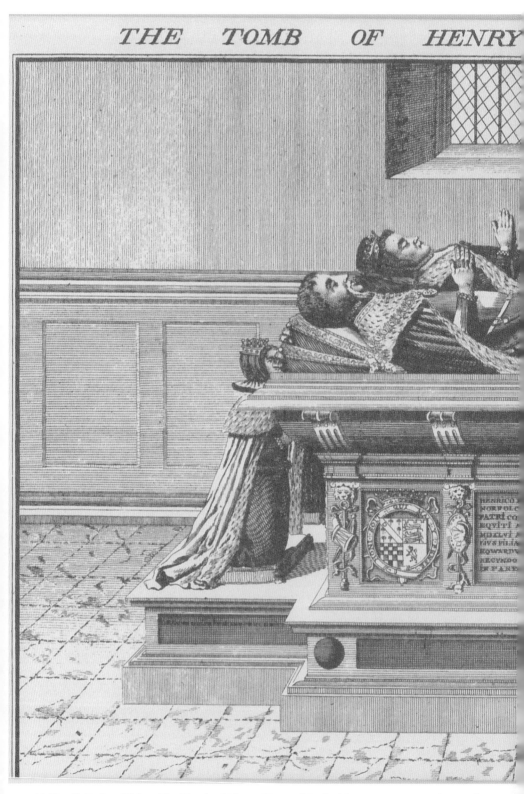

11 (Ford). Joshua Kirby, 'The Tomb of Henry Howard Earl of Surry', 1748, Joseph Wood, engrav
Archive of The Church of St. Michael Framlingham.

WARD EARL OF SURRY.

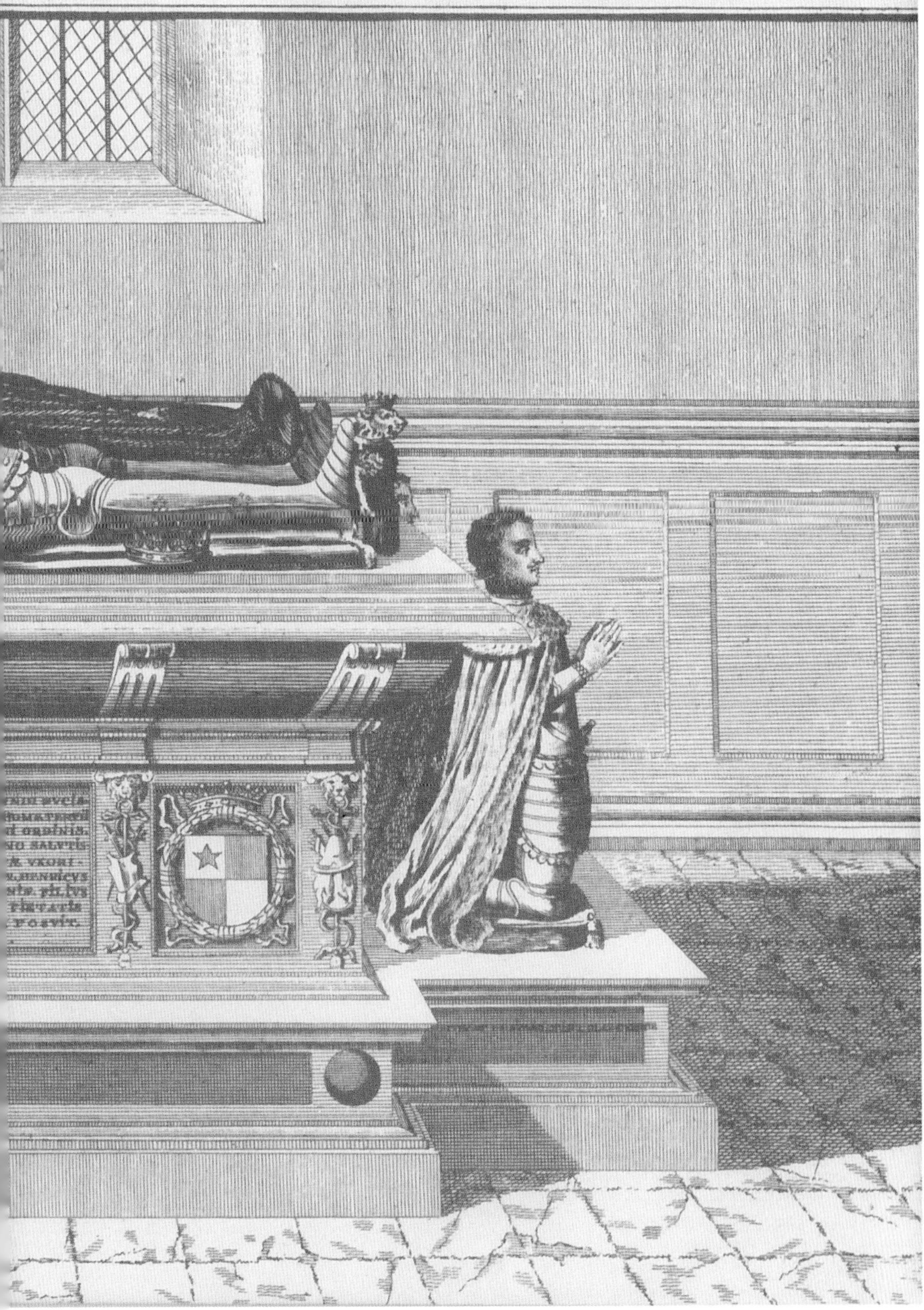

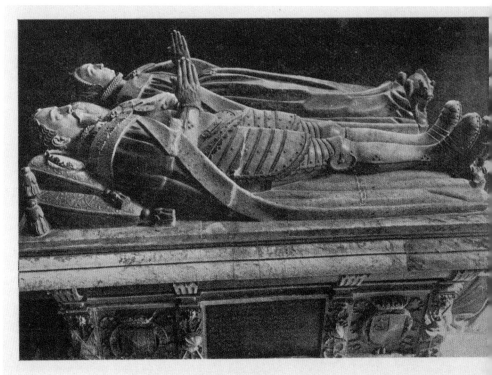

FIG. 45. FRAMLINGHAM, SUFFOLK: TOMB OF HENRY HOWARD, EARL OF SURREY, 1614.

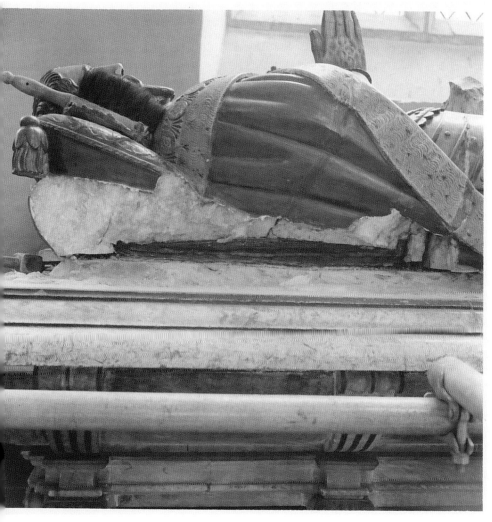

14 (Ford). Photo of Surrey tomb, c. 1976/7, during restoration, The Church of St. Michael, Framlingham, Suffolk, with the old coronet resting next to the handbrush by the effigy's head. Archive of The Church of St. Michael Framlingham.

(Ford, opposite, above)). Photo of Surrey tomb, The Church of St. Michael, Framlingham, Suffolk, with coronet near head of effigy, from J. Charles Cox, English Church Fittings, Furniture & Accessories (London 1923), 62.

(Ford, opposite, below). Holes in cushion supporting head of Surrey's effigy Surrey tomb, The Church of St. Michael, Framlingham, Suffolk (Lisa Ford).

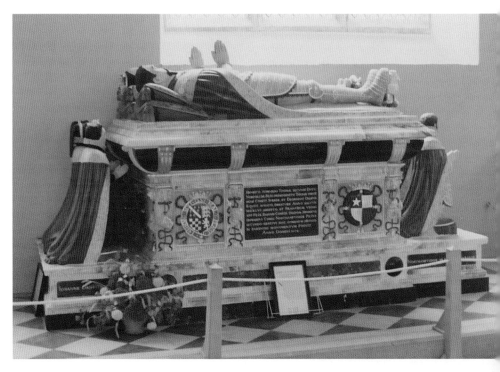

15 (Ford). Photo of Surrey tomb, c. 1976/7, immediately after restoration, The Church of St. Michael, Framlingham, Suffolk, without coronet.
Archive of The Church of St. Michael Framlingham.

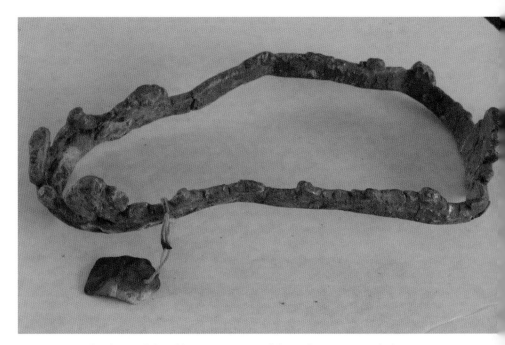

16 (Ford). Photo of the old coronet removed from the Surrey tomb during restoration.
Archive of The Church of St. Michael Framlingham (Lisa Ford).

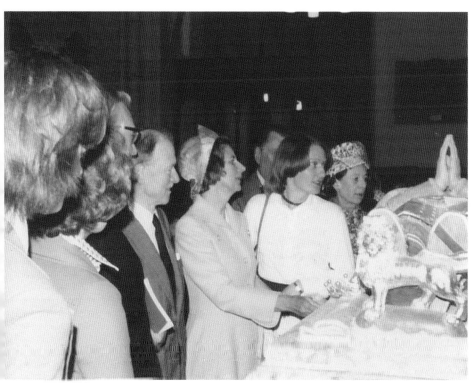

17 (Ford). Photo from service of reconsecration of Surrey tomb, 9 July, 1977
at The Church of St. Michael, Framlingham, Suffolk.
Archive of The Church of St. Michael, Framlingham.

(Ford). Tomb of Thomas Coventry, 1st Earl of Coventry. Church of St. Mary, Elmley Castle,
Worcester. Photo courtesy of Church Monuments Society.

19 (Ford, overleaf). Tomb of Henry Howard, Earl of Surrey, c. 1638,
from Henry Lilly MS, G 1/16, f. 128, Arundel Castle Archives.
By kind permission of His Grace the Duke of Norfolk.

at Lambeth had already been taken by 1542. Professor Marks has speculated that she had made this choice even before the priory's dissolution, but it seems more likely to be a direct consequence of the uncertainty engendered by that event.[56] We can conjecture that the third duke took the decision to exhume his father's body from the abandoned priory church, to move it to Lambeth and to commission a brass to mark the new burial place (the duke's brass is also illustrated in the *Howard Genealogy*), when duchess Agnes died in 1545.[57] This would explain why those investigating heraldry in the former Priory in December 1546 did not mention the second duke's monument: by then it had been dismantled for the removal of the duke's body. Nothing now survives at Thetford of the second duke's original monument save for the brick vault beneath it, in the ruined choir.[58] There was no coffin in the vault when it was cleared by the Office of Works in 1935, confirming that the body had already been moved.[59] The vault is now filled with sand. However, small fragments of painted heraldry which are perhaps from the monument – though they have never previously been identified – were excavated in the 1930s and are now on exhibition in Framlingham Castle.[60]

Duchess Agnes had chosen before 1542 to be interred at Lambeth and was actually interred there in 1545. The exhumation of her late husband's body, the dismantling of his monument and his reburial at Lambeth under a newly commissioned brass in 1545–6 definitively ended the use of Thetford Priory church as a Howard burial site. By now, the third duke had determined that the parish church of St Michael's, Framlingham should be the new location for his own and Richmond's expensive but still incomplete tomb-monuments. The decision to abandon Thetford will not have been taken lightly, but the destruction of the religious houses had removed the heart of the town's medieval economic and social structure, already under strain in the early sixteenth century. The Anglo-Norman motte and bailey castle (Fig. 14) had been abandoned as a military site centuries before and had never been a Howard residence. Framlingham, by contrast, was the location of the duke's great castle (Fig. 15) and deer park, the main centre of his power and influence in the east of Suffolk. Evidence survives from after the third duke's fall of his recent decisions. A certificate written by the churchwardens at Framlingham, dated 11 November 1547,

[56] Marks, 257.

[57] Manning, 'Brasses'. Lilly's manuscript is described by A. J. Horwood in the appendix to the *3rd Report of the Royal Commission on Historical Manuscripts*, reproduced in Manning's paper.

[58] Dymond (ed.), *Register*, I, 38. Marks, 257 revises Stone & Colvin, 162.

[59] Stone & Colvin, 162.

[60] Other unpublished fragments of effigies and tomb-chests, including alabaster, bear witness to the rich collection of tomb-monuments the church had once housed. I shall discuss these in our forthcoming monograph.

records that they had sold the church plate for £50: 'Th'wiche we intende to bestowe upon the buildynge up of the Churche, th'wich Churche my Lord of Norf. did pluke Downe to thintent to make yt bygger'.[61] A survey from 1549 confirms that that the duke had indeed 'plucked down' the old chancel of Framlingham church and its aisles. At this date, the chancel was apparently still 'not yet all builded up again. Also [...] certain lead was taken off the said Church with glass, boards and timber appertaining to the said Church lying in ye Castle aforesaid, and much of ye said timber is ready framed for ye use of the same Church'.[62] So, the chancel had been demolished and work had begun on rebuilding it on a larger scale before the duke's fall in December 1546, but work was then incomplete, probably implying that it had not been underway for more than a year or two. The only plausible reason for rebuilding the chancel on such a large scale is that the duke planned to house his tomb and that of his son-in-law in it. Indeed, given the substantial size of the new building (Figs 16, 17), it may have been his intention to retrieve some of the earlier monuments from Thetford, or to plan for the future by providing ample space for further Howard memorials. Whatever the case, the new chancel was not finished by the time of the duke's fall. Building then stopped abruptly and by the time of the churchwardens' certificate, Surrey had been executed, the duke was in prison, where he was to remain throughout Edward VI's reign, and the prospects of the Howard family looked very bleak.

After the fall of the Howards, Lord Protector Somerset was granted Thetford Priory and its estates, on 23 July 1547. However, less than a month later he leased them to Richard Fulmerston for 21 years. Fulmerston was a land agent and trusted servant of the Howards, who had defended the duke and Surrey at trial from accusations of treasonable activity and was himself now based in Thetford. By 1541, he had purchased the property of the four other religious houses in Thetford (the former Benedictine nunnery of St George which he converted into his own residence; the Priory of the Holy Sepulchre; and the Dominican and Augustinian friaries).[63] An arbitration award of 30 April 1554 between Fulmerston and the duke returned the site to the latter and in 1557 the former entered into an indenture to fulfil the terms of the award.[64]

61 PRO [TNA] E 315/510/62, cited by Stone & Colvin, 161, n. 13.
62 Stone & Colvin, 161, n.12. For its date, see 166. Green, *History*, 116, dates this survey 1553, in error for 1549. The date is 1549 in R. Green, *Guide to Framlingham*, Framlingham 1895, 29.
63 *L&P*, XIV/1 (1539), no. 651 (46). In c.1552 a valuation of the duke's former possessions was undertaken [PRO E 310/3/19]. The Dominican Friary, St Mary the Great, is the site of the Grammar School. See A. Crosby, *A History of Thetford*, Chichester 1986, 34, fig. 6.
64 Stone & Colvin, 161 n. 9 cite T. Martin, *History of the Town of Thetford*, London 1779, 48–9. See also Crosby, *Thetford*, 57.

What had happened to the monuments for the third duke and for Richmond in this tumultuous period? The duke had claimed that both were close to completion in 1539, but neither had been finished or set up. He must have ordered the immediate cessation of work in 1540 in the uncertain situation following the abbey's dissolution for, as we have seen, neither is mentioned by those investigating the heraldry of the monuments in the church in December 1546. Until very recently, this marked the end of the contemporary documentary trail. However, a recent discovery by Dr Kate Adcock in the inventories of the third duke's goods after his fall provides new evidence. In the inventories of his possessions at Kenninghall she noticed that after the third duke's fall, included amongst 'diverse and sondry other trasshe' was 'ffreestone of a Tombe' (Fig. 18).[65] A missing phase in the story can now be reconstructed. Some time after the dissolution, probably in 1545 or 1546, Howard had the unfinished tomb components moved for safe-keeping to his house at Kenninghall, pending the reconstruction of the chancel at Framlingham, to which he proposed to move them. However, to ascertain exactly what was stored and moved, we now need to turn back to the monuments at Framlingham.

Norfolk and Richmond's Monuments as Salvage or New Works: a False Dichotomy

The eighteenth-century antiquary Francis Blomefield believed that the monuments of the third duke and of Richmond at Framlingham had been moved from Thetford. Blomefield, who confusingly misidentifies the third duke's monument as that of his father, writes:

> At the Dissolution, the Bones of the Duke were taken up, and carried with his Freestone Monument to the church of St. *Michael*, at *Framlingham* in *Suffolk*, where it now remains, on the South-side of the altar. It hath no inscription now, but at each Corner there is a Lyon Sedant, supporting a Shield, on which are the arms of *Howard*, with that honourable Augmentation which the King gave him for his service at *Floddon-Field* [...] the 12 Apostles are neatly carved round the Tomb, and on the Top lies his own Effigies, by that of *Agnes*, Daughter of Sir *Philip Tilney*, Knt. his second Wife, who was buried in *Lambeth* church in *Surrey*.

Of Fitzroy's monument, he states:

> Henry Fitz-Roy [...] died at St. *James, July* 22, 1536, and was buried in this Church [Thetford]; but at the Dissolution his Body and Monument were removed, with his Father-in-Law's, to *Framlingham* aforesaid, where it now remains on the North-side of the Altar, it is of freestone, garnished round with divers Histories of the Bible, and on the top were 12 Figures,

---

[65] TNA, LR2/115 (the 1551 version of the inventory), folio 64r. I owe this reference to Dr Kate Adcock.

each supporting a Trophy of the Passion, but all of them, are miserably defaced, his Arms in the Garter, with a ducal Coronet over them, are still perfect.[66]

Setting aside Blomefield's misidentification of the third duke's monument, what is important is his assertion that the two monuments at Framlingham that we identify as those of the third duke and of Richmond had both been moved from Thetford Priory. He additionally records what must also have been an oral tradition that there were originally intended to be twelve figures on top of Richmond's tomb-chest, describing it as if the figures were still there but defaced. In fact, only four figures were visible as other evidence proves.

Thomas Martin in his posthumously published *History of Thetford,* did not discuss the third duke's monument, confining himself to Richmond's, but confirming the story of its move from Thetford. He wrote:

> At the dissolution his bones were removed hence to Framlingham, with his monument, which now stands on the north side of the altar. It has no inscription nor effigies, but at each corner is a figure holding a shield, and the instruments of the passion; the cornice is charged with compartments of Old Testament history. On the north side twice, and once on the south, are his wife's arms in a lozenge. At the east and west end, and twice on the south side, his arms, England, with a baton sinister and Talbois on a scutcheon of pretence, impaling Howard; also England with Talbois in a garter ducally crowned ...[67]

It is revealing that he does not repeat Blomefield's description of twelve figures on top of the monument, mentioning only four.

Robert Hawes and Robert Loder in *The History of Framlingham* begun by Hawes in 1712, edited and completed by Loder and published in 1798, describe and illustrate the monuments but do not report the tradition that they were moved from Thetford.[68] Hawes identifies the Howard monument as that of the third duke and his first or second wife, finally opting for the latter.

Richard Green, in his 1834 *History of Framlingham*, developed an argument of teasing complexity and preposterous implausibility. He notes that the monument we ascribe to the third duke was assigned by Blomefield to the second duke and by Hawes to the third duke; Martin, he correctly observed, had said that the second duke's monument had been destroyed.[69] Green attempted to reconcile these statements by arguing that the tomb was indeed that of the *second* duke, and 'that it was ... brought from Thetford.' However, he went on,

---

[66]   F. Blomefield, *An Essay Towards a Topographical History of the County of Norfolk,* I, Fersfield 1739, 455.
[67]   Martin, *Thetford,* London 1779, 124.
[68]   R. Hawes & R. Loder, *The History of Framlingham,* Woodbridge 1798, 301–3.
[69]   Martin, *History,* 123.

'subsequently the effigy of the second duke was removed to make room for that of his son the third duke [... and] the effigy of a Duchess, which, contrary to monumental usage, lies to the right of the duke, is that of Agnes his mother-in-law, and not that of either of his wives'.[70] By 1895, however, the date of the [posthumous] publication of the fourth edition of Green's church guide, this unwieldy argument had been abandoned and the monument was assigned wholly to the third duke and his second wife.[71] About Richmond's monument, there was no argument. Green followed Blomefield and Martin in stating that it had been brought from Thetford, and after detailing the heraldry and the subject matter of the reliefs adds: 'There were anciently eight other figures on the top corresponding with those at each of the corners'.[72] This must go back to Blomefield.

In the nineteen-thirties, James Mann saw the four tombs as a group by themselves. He related the effigies to those of the second earl of Huntingdon and his countess at Ashby de la Zouche, Leicestershire – suggesting they might be the work of a Midlands carver – and the tomb-chests to Lord Brooke's at Cobham.[73] He suggested they were the work of artists specially brought in to work on the spot. Katharine Esdaile, in her book of 1946, made the same connection with Cobham but also cited a very wide range of other comparisons, including the Marney tombs at Layer Marney in Essex. She further argued that the apostles of the third duke's tomb should be compared with the freestone statues of saints inside Henry VII's chapel, Westminster: 'it seems certain,' she thought, 'that an Englishman who had worked under Torrigiani was responsible for both sets of monuments'.[74] Such a comparison – the Henry VII figures are quite different in style and date from much earlier in Henry VIII's reign – did not really advance the subject.[75]

---

[70] Green, *History*, 132. He identifies the apostles as *North: Stephen, Thomas, doubtful, Mathias; West: Peter, doubtful, Paul; South: Andrew, Simon, James the Less, doubtful; East: Bartholomew, doubtful, John.*

[71] Green, *Guide to Framlingham*, fourth edition, 1895, 24, the argument being that if the monument had been erected by the fourth duke, he would naturally have commemorated his own grandmother, not the duke's first wife. His grandmother, however, was buried at Lambeth and Duchess Anne had been buried at Thetford. She is much the likelier candidate for the effigy.

[72] Ibid., 133.

[73] J. G. Mann, 'English Church Monuments, 1536–1625', *Walpole Society* 21, (1932–33), 1–22 (7).

[74] K. A. Esdaile, *English Church Monuments 1510 to 1840*, London 1946, 56 and 59.

[75] P. Lindley, 'The Singuler Mediacions and Praiers of all the Holie Companie of Heven': Sculptural Functions and Forms in Henry VII's Chapel', in T. Tatton-Brown and R. Mortimer (eds), *Westminster Abbey: the Lady Chapel of Henry VII*, Boydell & Brewer, Woodbridge 2003, 259–93.

By contrast, a major contribution was made by Margaret Whinney, the path-breaking historian of post-Reformation sculpture in Britain. She offered a subtle if frustratingly laconic interpretation of the monuments, in a discussion whose brevity must have been necessitated by the huge chronological and geographical range of materials she had to cover in her monograph. Whilst she accepted the view that both monuments had been moved to Framlingham from Thetford, she also contended they had been *completed* in the 1560s. In other words, the monuments transported from Thetford had been unfinished works. She identified some components – such as the narrative reliefs on Richmond's monument – as work of the 1530s, whilst other elements, for example the Doric pilasters on Richmond's tomb-chest below the reliefs, were later. The effigies on the third duke's tomb were identical in style to those of the fourth duke's wives and therefore belonged to the same date. In short, she argued that the monuments were composites, constructed in two phases: they were begun in the late 1530s but only finished in the 1560s.[76]

Two other great scholars, Lawrence Stone and Howard Colvin, writing at almost exactly the same time, articulated a view of the monuments which was wholly incompatible with Whinney's.[77] In a brilliant paper published in 1965, they argued that the monuments of the third duke and of Richmond were *entirely* works of the 1550s. *Nothing* of the monuments reported to be nearly complete in 1539 had survived (they never conjectured what had happened to these expensive but unfinished works). Stone and Colvin offered five new, specifically art-historical, arguments in support of their theory that the third duke's and Richmond's monuments were made in the 1550s. First, they noted the repetition of the same two masons' marks (Fig. 19) – that is to say, the marks which identified the individual responsible for carving each block of stone – on the third duke's, Richmond's, and the fourth duke's monuments. Second, they noticed two contemporary graffito dates on the monuments, neither of which had ever been identified before: 1555 on Richmond's monument (Fig. 20) and 1559 on the third duke's.[78] The evident stylistic connection between all four of the monuments rendered it wholly improbable, they argued, that there could be a twenty-year gap between the first and last. Fourth, the collar round the neck of the effigy of the third duke (Fig. 21) with its motto: 'Gracia Dei sum quod sum' referred, they believed, to the duke's providential release from prison under Mary.[79] Finally, the duchess's effigy was shown wearing a ruff (Fig. 22), a fashion

[76] M. Whinney, *Sculpture in Britain 1530–1830*, Harmondsworth 1964, 7 and 232, notes 17–19.
[77] This is the more surprising as they, like Margaret Whinney, were deeply indebted for their knowledge of French stylistic comparanda to Anthony Blunt.
[78] These are discussed by Rebecca Constabel, below.
[79] This argument is derived from Green, *History*, p. 81, note, but Stone & Colvin were

60

first introduced under Queen Mary.[80] In addition to these striking visual observations, they also offered two historical arguments in favour of their theory. First, the inherent improbability that the monuments could simply have been stored at Thetford between the dissolution and the 1550s: they could not have been placed in the chancel at Framlingham because it was not ready in 1549 and was probably still not complete as late as 1557 (the evidence for which was a request from the churchwardens for a warrant to finish the church).[81] Second, the fact that the third duke, in his will of 1554, did not mention his monument, leaving the selection of his burial site to his executors.[82] So, they concluded, *all* the monuments – Richmond's and the third duke's and then the fourth duke's and the infant Elizabeth's – had been made as a sequential series in the 1550s and 1560s. What is absolutely remarkable is that they never discussed Whinney's theory that the third duke's and Richmond's monuments were two-phase objects, even though they certainly knew her work.[83] Of course, her book's publication was very close in date to their paper and it is possible they simply did not have enough time to digest its implications.

There was, however, one major obstacle to their whole argument of which Stone and Colvin were acutely aware. This was the style of a number of sculpted tomb components which had been discovered in clearance excavations at Thetford in 1935, within a detached sacristy on the north side of the priory church, and which Stone and Colvin themselves published for the first time (Figs 23–27). These fragments, free of mortar, and so never actually assembled, 'were,' they recognised, 'clearly intended for a tomb. They are the work of the same group of sculptors who worked on the tombs of the duke of Richmond and the third duke of Norfolk now at Framlingham'.[84] The pieces comprised three components of a detached shaft, on which four small Old Testament figures were carved integrally with the architecture (Fig. 23); four components of a closely related half-shaft and base, evidently from a tomb-chest (Fig. 24); a piece of architectural moulding from the top of a tomb-chest, carved with a hybrid form of egg-and-dart; some other architectural details from the tomb-chest; fragments of volutes from capitals; a pair of kneeling (but unfortunately headless) angels holding coats of arms with Instruments of the Passion (a type of heraldry assigned to Christ in the later middle ages) (Figs. 25, 26); a relief panel, showing an angel with the three Magi (Fig. 27); and, finally, a painted figure holding an

---

aware of its unreliability (166, n. 21).

[80] Stone & Colvin, 166–7.
[81] Stone & Colvin, 166, n. 20.
[82] Green, *History*, 81. Head, *Ebbs & Flows*, 343, n. 65, cites the will from TNA Probate 11/37/103–5, which I have not consulted.
[83] E.g. in Stone & Colvin, 169, it is cited twice in footnotes.
[84] Stone & Colvin, 163.

open book towards the viewer (Fig. 41).

It was – and is – logical to assume that any pieces excavated on the priory site were carved *before* the dissolution in 1540. However, Stone and Colvin were committed to the belief that Richmond's and the third duke's monuments were only carved in the 1550s. Still, they recognized that the stylistic case for associating the excavated pieces with the third duke's and Richmond's tombs was unanswerable. So, logically, they were now constrained to argue that sculptors were working in Thetford, on the priory site, a decade and a half *after* its dissolution – that is to say between 1554 and 1559 – carving Norfolk's tomb and Richmond's, together with parts of a *third* tomb. Such an argument obviously necessitated some very special pleading. To perhaps the most obvious question – what sculptors were doing working at Thetford in the 1550s, some fifteen years after the priory had been dissolved – they answered that there must have been plans to revive a monastic community at Thetford Priory under Mary. Then, after Elizabeth's accession at the end of 1558, when it became clear that no such revival would take place, the first two monuments were moved to Framlingham, where the same sculptors subsequently produced the monuments of the fourth duke's wives and of his daughter. This theory raised further awkward questions. To take just two of them: why had the excavated pieces been abandoned at Thetford; and to whose monument did they belong? Stone and Colvin proffered two different suggestions: first that the pieces might have belonged to a tomb planned to commemorate the earl of Surrey who had been executed in 1547, a commission which was then abandoned for some unknown reason; or that they belonged to an earlier scheme for the third duke's monument, which was precipitously abandoned when the sculptor responsible for the Apostles turned up in Thetford.[85]

It is extremely difficult to believe that this theory can have really satisfied its eminent authors and the changes of location for the third duke's burial site and monument which their suggestion would have necessitated – Thetford, Framlingham, Thetford again and then, finally, Framlingham once more – are bewildering to contemplate. An uncharacteristic frustration can certainly be detected in some of their paper's phraseology. Before we leave their argument, though, we must bring one other piece of evidence into the equation, with which – had they known of it – Stone and Colvin would certainly have been able to strengthen their case. This is the existence, hitherto unpublished, of six fragments of an armoured tomb-effigy, uncovered in the same 1930s Thetford excavations, which must surely be associated with either Richmond's or Norfolk's effigy. The sabaton (Fig. 28) has diagnostic features – the closely spaced articulation of the lames in particular – which are very difficult to parallel before the mid-sixteenth

[85] Stone & Colvin, 168.

century and Dr Tobias Capwell of the Wallace Collection, who has kindly given me his opinion on the basis of photographs, very much doubts whether comparanda can be found earlier than c. 1560 and is inclined to opt for an even later date. If it is the case that, in effigial sculpture in England, the pieces fit most readily with a date in the 1550s, or even later, then Stone and Colvin's argument that the workshop responsible for the third duke's and Richmond's monument were at work in Thetford in the 1550s receives important support.[86] However, the features of the carved effigy may directly reflect the very latest armour of c. 1540, which the third duke and Surrey were certainly buying at the time, and which could have been furnished to the sculptor as a model, given the duke's close personal involvement in the commission. It would be unwise to rely too heavily on it as evidence for a workshop's operation at Thetford in the 1550s.

The tomb components Stone and Colvin published had already been carefully studied by the excavators in the 1930s. They had themselves immediately realised that there was a very close relationship between the excavated fragments and the monuments of the third duke and of Richmond at Framlingham. William Ormsby-Gore (fourth Baron Harlech from 1938), First Commissioner of Works between 1931 and 1936, discussed the materials they had uncovered in an unpublished 1936 paper.[87] He quoted G. H. Chettle of the Office of Works, who had produced some wonderful, if highly conjectural, reconstruction drawings (Figs 29, 30), incorporating the excavated pieces (one of these drawings was later published by Stone and Colvin). Chettle had stated:

> The fragments consist of moulded and sculptured blocks of clunch. These blocks retain the mason's setting-out lines scored on their surface but show no trace of mortar [n]or any indication that they were ever assembled as a structural whole ... Unfortunately, the material which has been found at Thetford does not provide us with complete evidence on which to base a reconstruction of the tomb. We can only guess at the total height, the mouldings of the base, and the treatment of the main panels between the attached shafts ... In the setting-out of the design as a whole the resemblance to the tomb of the third Duke of Norfolk is striking. The upper part of the base, the bases of the shafts, the shafts themselves, might all be the work of the same designer. The insertion of sculptured panels in the frieze recalls the Fitzroy tomb, but the execution of the Fitzroy panels is superior. The Angels on the corners of the Fitzroy tomb are recalled by the angels found at Thetford.

Ormsby-Gore followed Chettle, commending 'his skilful reconstruction of the tomb'. Agreeing that 'the fragments were destined for the tomb of a high personage, that they show remarkable resemblances of detail to both the Fitzroy

[86] My thanks to Dr Capwell for his information on dating.
[87] My thanks to Dr Hall for supplying me with a xerox of this paper. I shall give more extended consideration to Chettle's reconstructions at a later date.

tomb and that of the third duke of Norfolk at Framlingham and that in all probability they were never assembled as a structural whole,' he discussed for whom tomb this might have been intended. First, he suggested that the pieces might have been fragments of an unfinished tomb for the third duke, abandoned at the Dissolution. However, Ormsby-Gore noted the similarities between the New Testament relief of the three Magi, and the pair of angels on the one hand, and the Old Testament reliefs and figures of Richmond's monument at Framlingham on the other. So, he wavered, perhaps they had been intended instead for Richmond's tomb? But next he also suggested that the pieces could have belonged to a monument for the third duke intended to complement Richmond's. In evident bewilderment, he concluded, unhappily: 'It is impossible to say whether it was the tomb of the duke of Richmond or [of] the third duke of Norfolk but it seems extremely probable that it was the tomb of one of these two'. What he did not consider was the possibility that the excavated pieces might include components from *both* tombs.

Nearly twenty years after Stone and Colvin's paper, Professor Marks published a new examination of the whole problem, prompted by his discovery of a representation of the lost tomb of Thomas the second duke (d. 1524) in the collections of Thomas Wriothesley, Garter King of Arms (mentioned above in our discussion of the second duke's monument). Marks also realised that two figural panels in the British Museum – bust-length reliefs of an Old Testament prophet and a king holding scrolls – excavated at Thetford in the nineteenth century, belonged with the pieces unearthed in the 1930s (Figs 31, 32).[88] A fragmentary piece of a similar bust found in 1935 was, as he showed, from the same series of reliefs (Fig. 33). Marks returned to Whinney's suggestion that the Framlingham tombs of the third duke and of Richmond were constructed in two phases, the first being when, in 1539, they were carved at Thetford and were intended to stand in the priory church. The second phase, after the Dissolution, belonged to the 1550s and was executed at Framlingham. He noted that the masons' marks identified by Stone and Colvin appeared only in the second phase of work, not on any of the earlier material. To this second phase, he assigned the effigies of the third duke and his wife, which he thought were the work of the same sculptors who were responsible for the effigies of the fourth duke's wives.[89] With them he placed the caryatid herms on Richmond's monument. He grouped three of the lions of the third duke's monument with those of the fourth duke and the (lower) tomb-chest of Richmond's monument also with that of the fourth duke. These components he dated between 1555 and 1559 – the dates incised on

[88]   Marks, 252–68. The reliefs may have been excavated by Henry Harrod in 1849, though he does not mention them: H. Harrod, *Gleanings among the Castles and Convents of Norfolk*, Norwich 1857, 14–23.

[89]   Marks, 260.

the monuments – as confirmed by the masons' marks which appeared on the architectural components and on the heraldic shields of Fitzroy's monument. To the earlier phase he allocated the 'angels and Old Testament panels on the Fitzroy tomb' and the apostles on the third duke's monument. Marks linked the phase 1 work with the components excavated at Thetford, bringing the British Museum panels and the related fragment into the discussion for the first time. He identified the New Testament relief as belonging to the third duke's monument and concluded: 'The two tombs would together have presented the Old Law and the New, one with Old Testament prophets, kings and scenes, the other with the apostles and episodes from the New Testament'.[90]

Marks's proposal did not find favour with Professor William A. Sessions, in his biography of Surrey.[91] Sessions instead followed Stone and Colvin in assigning the fragments excavated at Thetford to a third tomb, destined for Surrey. He maintained that 'before 1540, or shortly thereafter, Surrey designed his own tomb at Thetford Priory to complement Richmond's. The two tombs then would exist in a loving counterpoint that his father's tomb (in his son's designs) later took on with Richmond's. If this is so', he concludes, 'then quite possibly Surrey had a strong hand in originating the initial design of the tombs at Framlingham'.[92] However, this suggestion must be rejected: there is no evidence that Surrey was concerned with the monuments at all, let alone contemplating his own tomb – he was still in his early twenties – nor that *three* rather than *two* monuments were ever planned; the dating assigned to their construction is certainly wrong, their materials are misidentified and Sessions' argument, however seductive, seems internally inconsistent.[93] By contrast Marks's paper – a revision and development of Whinney's view, bringing additional material into the discussion for the first time – seems persuasive, and offers a valuable starting point for our own structural analysis of the monuments.

Virtual Deconstruction and Reconstruction: Realising the Unfinished

Sir John Pope-Hennessy, one of the greatest connoisseurs of Italian sculpture, offered some valuable insights into its study in his autobiography: 'Sculptures cannot be looked at rapidly; they must be recorded slowly and seen repeatedly,' he wrote. 'The longer I looked at them, the more vital did it seem to regard them as things made and to reconstruct the process by which they were produced'.

[90]   Marks, 262. The Magi panel is connected with the second duke's monument by F. J. E. Raby, P. K. Baillie Reynolds and S. E. Rigold, *Thetford Priory, Norfolk*, London 1979, caption 10, though this is inconsistent with their text, 7, where it is assigned to the third duke's.

[91]   W. A. Sessions, *Henry Howard, the Poet Earl of Surrey. A Life*, Oxford 1999, 119–123.

[92]   Ibid., 123.

[93]   Sessions states that the Framlingham tombs are made from marble.

He adds, 'I learned two things of importance, that no knowledge was absolute and that there were no shortcuts'.[94] What is certainly true for the individual scholar's gradual apprehension of sculptural form and material structure through repeated visual study and cogitation seems to me also to be true of scholarship in general.[95]

The present project aimed to analyse the monuments in Pope-Hennessy's terms as 'things made' and to 'reconstruct the process[es] by which they were produced' – even though these processes had never been completed. 3D laser scanning was employed to virtually disassemble the monuments at Framlingham, to distinguish phases of construction, and to reintegrate the pieces excavated at Thetford in hypothetical reconstructions of the monuments as originally intended. A preliminary step in differentiating the constructional phases was a stone-by-stone analysis of the third duke's and of Richmond's monument which a skilled archaeological draughtswoman, Jill Atherton, undertook with me. The dimensions of each stone were recorded. Visual examination of the structures, the work of previous scholars discussed above, the presence of masons' marks on the components assigned to the 1550s by virtue of their graffiti dates and comparisons with the monument of the fourth duke, the stylistic distinction between the phases – in the direction of a flatter, more linear and more 'advanced' style (by which is meant closer to classical architectural norms) – as well as the hitherto unnoticed employment of a different stone for the later phase of work from the clunch employed in 1539, helped me discriminate between the first campaign undertaken at Thetford and the later one, when the monuments were 'finished off' at Framlingham in the 1550s. The clunch sometimes has small flint inclusions which are occasionally physically and visually obtrusive, as is the case with 'the drunkenness of Noah' (Fig. 34), one of the Old Testament reliefs on Richmond's monument, and in places in the Apostle reliefs on the third duke's. What was evident is that tomb-chest of the third duke's monument was essentially from the Thetford phase; the plain upper section, effigies and heraldic beasts were later. By contrast, the Old Testament reliefs and the figures on the corners of the tomb-chest were the only parts salvaged from the c.1539 project for Richmond's monument.

With this in mind, we can return again to the mention of 'ffreestone of a

[94] J. Pope-Hennessy, *Learning to See*, London 1991, 115–16.
[95] An idealised account of the progress of art-historical knowledge might see it as analogous to the process of scientific understanding envisaged by Sir Karl Popper: the empirical testing of hypotheses and their modification or replacement by new hypotheses as a result. However, given scholars' retention of their hypotheses in the face of contradictory evidence, perhaps the subject moves in a way more similar to Thomas Kuhn's account of 'normal science' in *The Structure of Scientific Revolutions,* where theories are preserved and applied until a paradigm shift is forced in a period of revolutionary change.

Tombe' in the Kenninghall inventory found by Dr Adcock. All the pieces of the monuments at Framlingham which can be identified as originating in the pre-Dissolution phase 1 would together only have comprised enough material for a single tomb, and would not have included any effigies: we know that a good number of components had been abandoned at Thetford. What was stored at Kenninghall must have comprised the tomb-chest with the Apostles from the third duke's monument, and the Old Testament reliefs and standing angels from Richmond's. It would have been perfectly logical for the writer of the inventory to assume that these were all parts of a single monument. In reality, what he saw comprised components not of *one* tomb but parts of *two*.[96]

Close visual analysis of the construction of both monuments at Framlingham sheds a good deal of new light on them. For example, the damage suffered by the monument of the third duke as a consequence of its moves is revealed by evidence of breakages and losses. This is most clear when one considers the substantial blocks of stone from which the apostles standing in shell-headed niches, on the sides of the tomb-chest, are carved. Many of these blocks have suffered damage to the shell niches, often in the same approximate location (or its mirror-image, reverse), perhaps implying that one large quarried block from which several panels were carved had a flaw in this area, along which the panels broke when they were transported. In some cases repair was possible but in other instances the damaged piece was replaced using a different stone (Fig. 35): this is the limestone employed in the 1550s to complete the monuments at Framlingham. This change of stone was therefore diagnostically significant. If the monument's components had been moved from Thetford to Kenninghall across Tudor roads and then, again, after several years in storage, from Kenninghall to Framlingham, the unanticipated extra handling and carriage will explain why the apostle panels suffered damage. It is true that some tomb-monuments of the period, notably alabaster ones, were safely conveyed considerable distances from where they had been carved to their destinations, where they were set up. There are very good reasons, though, to think that the monuments of the third duke and of Richmond were originally carved at Thetford, probably even within the priory precincts, near the locations they were planned to occupy, and were never planned to be transported any distance. Clunch suitable for construction of monuments is available in and near Thetford and was certainly being quarried in the sixteenth century.[97] The blocks from

---

[96]   It seems impossible that the third duke could have been thinking of combining the salvaged components in a single work because they would not fit together either in terms of subject matter or dimensions.

[97]   R. L. S. Bruce-Mitford, 'A Late-Medieval Chalk-Mine at Thetford', *Norfolk Archaeology*, XXX (1952), 220–2; H. Dixon Hewitt, 'Chalk Mines at Thetford', *Norfolk Archaeology*, XXXI (1957), 231–2.

which the standing apostles were carved are so big that they must have been extremely heavy and could only have been moved with difficulty.[98] Given that the material from which they are made is easily damaged, this also suggests that the relief figures were carved very close to where they were to be erected. For, had it been originally intended to transport them any distance, it would have been a simple matter to have carved the panels in separate, smaller pieces. Fascinatingly, this was precisely the way two of the panels from the east end of the monument were carved. The narrow central, Old Testament figure's block is a single piece, but the apostles on either side are each carved in two horizontal pieces. The joints between the blocks are not, though, in the same place: the image of St John the Evangelist is separated at his chin (Figs 36, 39), across the upper mouldings of the architecture below the shell niche whereas St Thomas has the joint at the waist. What should one make of these unique deviations from the procedures adopted for the rest of the standing figures? They are stylistically consistent with the rest of the figures, so there can be no question that they are the work of a different sculptor with different working methods. Nor is it at all probable that these blocks alone were sawn for ease of handling by those who later transported them. One possible explanation is that the figures were the first to be carved and that the sculptor quickly realized that carving them from separate pieces of stone was unnecessary, if they were only to be moved a short distance. However, an argument could also be made that these were the last figures to be carved, before the sculptor went on to produce the bust-length figures of Old Testament kings and prophets – now represented by the two panels from the British Museum and a fragment excavated in the 1930s – intended for Richmond's monument. By now, he may have run out of sufficiently large blocks, but this did not cause him problems because he was skilled enough to work with whatever pieces of stone were available to him. Many oddities of structure which demonstrate the sculptor's facility at using several blocks of stone as parts of the same relatively small narrative relief are exhibited by the Old Testament panels.[99] Of course, had the sculptures been painted as intended, the joints would have been invisible to the viewer.

The second phase of work saw the 3D laser-scanning of all four monuments by a commercial partner, Europac (Fig. 37), commissioned by the University of Leicester's Space Research Centre, directed by the late Professor George Fraser.[100] Our drawings and measurements of Richmond's and the third duke's monuments and the scanned data were delivered to the Physics doctoral student

[98]   This point was made to me by Prof Fraser.
[99]   Some features – such as the use of several panels of stone for the same narrative relief – are reminiscent of the skilled working of reliefs in the Lady Chapel at Ely, carved from the same material in the first half of the fourteenth century.
[100] This work was the subject of a competitive tendering process.

in the SRC, Nishad Karim, who, instructed by Piyal Samara-Ratna in the use of a Siemens CAD system, used the drawings to virtually disassemble the scanned monuments along the construction lines indicated in the dimensioned drawings Jill Atherton and I had provided (Figs 38, 39). This work proved that there was no substitute for on-site visual analysis, notwithstanding the sub-millimeter accuracy of the scanned data. Sometimes the 3D scan data were interpreted as implying constructional breaks where they were in fact moulding edges and it proved almost impossible to identify breaks between individual pieces of stone when the mortar between them was level with the stone surfaces, whereas this was easily done on site because of the colour differences between the mortar and the stone.

Next, the excavated pieces, which I had reidentified in English Heritage stores in 2006, and the panels in the British Museum (Fig. 40), were also scanned. These scanned pieces were then superimposed upon the 1930s reconstruction drawings, to identify exactly which pieces survived, whether any had been lost, and the accuracy or inaccuracy of Mr Chettle's reconstructions. Experience of the conventions of archaeological draughtsmen proved invaluable in interpreting and understanding his drawings. Chettle had silently multiplied some pieces which survived in order to enhance the viewer's understanding of the function of the individual components, but without indicating which elements were repetitions of the surviving pieces. He had also incorporated at least one piece – a seated figure – which from its style and the fact that it was painted, whereas none of the other pieces had been (painting usually occurring only after monuments were erected), ought to have been excluded: scanning confirmed my contention that it was also too large to fit into the position Chettle had assigned it (compare Figs 29 and 41). The third element of the work was to take the scanned fragments from Thetford and to integrate them with the scanned components of the monuments at Framlingham, with the objective of hypothesising what the monuments of the third duke and of Richmond were originally intended to look like within the priory church at Thetford in 1539. In other words, by attempting to complete Phase 1, the aim was to reconstruct what had actually been intended – but never realized – by the third duke and his workmen.

In attempting to reconstruct these intentions, I began with tentative hypotheses. First, that the phase 1 tomb-chest of the third duke's monument, as assembled at Framlingham, was always intended to be part of his monument, rather than of Richmond's (or Surrey's). There would need to be a strong reason to suppose that this was not the case, even though, in the absence of inscriptions, there is no absolute proof. The third duke had the monument salvaged from Thetford and placed in store at Kenninghall before his fall from power. When he was restored to his position under Mary, it is reasonable to suppose that he communicated his intentions to his grandson even if, at the time of his death, the components had not yet been moved to Framlingham for completion and setting in position. A second hypothesis, which we shall see is supported by stylistic, iconographic and technical considerations, is that the third duke's and Richmond's monuments were conceived and carved as a complementary pair. It seems inconceivable that the monument of the king's natural son, the duke of Richmond and Somerset, should have been intended to be lower in height than that of his father-in-law as it is today. Third, that Howard's monument was more advanced towards completion than its companion when work was stopped in 1540. The whole of the lower tomb-chest was evidently complete, whereas less of Richmond's monument could be salvaged, because less of it had been finished.

The three fragments of a baluster shaft found in the 1934–5 excavations at Thetford support this argument. Stylistically and technically, they are slightly more advanced than the columnar shafts surrounded by triple balusters of the third duke's tomb. The four figures on the main fragment of the fluted shaft, originally intended to stand at a corner of Richmond's monument, are carved from the same piece of stone as the shaft itself, whereas on the third duke's tomb, the trios of figures were carved separately and then attached to the shaft (Figs 11, 23). It looks like an earlier model. Only one figure on each baluster shaft survives today at Framlingham, facing inwards to the tomb-chest of the third duke. In 1841, when the narrow vault under the third duke's tomb was opened, the Reverend J. W. Darby noted:

> Amongst the rubbish in the vault were found fragments of two figures carved in stone, one holding an open book, the other a scroll of paper. Now several small figures have been removed from the pedestals at the 4 corners of the Monument, and from this it would seem probable that they were broken when removed from Thetford [as recorded] & thrown by the workmen into the vault.[101]

These figures have since been lost, but there seems no reason to doubt Darby's view that they belonged on the shafts. Figures holdings scrolls and books are seen amongst the four surviving in situ (Figs 11, 42). Previous commentators had not noticed that the head of one such figure was also found among the fragments excavated at Thetford (Fig. 43).[102] It is slightly larger than those of the

---

[101] J. Ashdown-Hill, 'The Opening of the Tombs of the Dukes of Richmond and Norfolk, Framlingham, April 1841, the Account of the Reverend J. W. Darby', *Ricardian*, 18 (2008), 100–7, note 1, referring to the manuscript as BL Additional MS 93 is incorrect: Additional MS numbers start only with 4101, as they continued from the numbers of the Sloanian Collection. The transcription is actually from Additional MS 19193.

[102] P. Lindley, *Thetford's Lost Tudor Sculptures*, Leicester 2013, a guide to accompany our exhibition in the Ancient House Museum, Thetford, first illustrated the head. The guide presents in condensed form some of the argument presented here.

figures on Richmond's baluster (Fig. 44). What its existence suggests is that although the baluster shafts of the third duke's monument were salvaged, some of these small figures were left behind and were not replaced when the monument was assembled and completed at Framlingham in the 1550s. When it was erected, the surviving figures were turned inwards to face the tomb-chest, so the absence of others would be less conspicuous and two figures left over or damaged were simply thrown into the vault as rubbish.

Today, of course, Richmond's monument is much shorter than the third duke's: its heraldry, coronets and the upper section with Old Testament narrative reliefs combined are roughly equivalent in height to the section with the apostles on the third duke's monument. However, the three components of Richmond's baluster indicate that the whole monument was originally intended to be of the same height as the third duke's monument and to match its general proportions. The half-shaft and base also excavated at Thetford strongly support this contention (Fig. 24). These components were intended to stand on a side or at an end of the tomb-chest, between sculpted figures or heraldic panels, dividing them architecturally. They very closely resemble those in place on the third duke's monument (Figs 1–3). Ormsby-Gore had noted, 'the upper part of the base, the bases of the shafts, the shafts themselves, might all be the work of the same designer' as the third duke's monument. In fact, they certainly are.

Can it be certainly determined whether the panels flanking the half-shafts were heraldic or featured imagery? We know that the third duke's monument, up to the top of the lower tomb-chest (i.e. below the panelled upper section) looks essentially as it was planned to in 1539. It has standing apostles on the sides of the tomb-chest (Fig. 45). Richmond's monument has heraldic shields surmounted by ducal coronets (many now very damaged and some cut back to the surface) on its lower tomb-chest, but all this part of the monument dates to the 1550s. However, even though the monument's current proportions, architecture and many details differ from what was envisaged in 1539, it is likely that Richmond's tomb-chest was always intended to feature his glamorous heraldry alongside that of his Howard wife. The second Howard duke's monument provided a crucial recent precedent for an heraldically-focussed tomb-chest. We have already seen that marriages and projected marriages ambitiously and dangerously tied the Howards to the Tudors – or alienated the monarchs – and further, that the treason charges which destroyed Surrey were based on his alleged arrogation of royal heraldry to himself. The ironic nature of these charges in view of the duke's post as Earl Marshal hardly needs emphasis. Certainly, the marital alliance with the king's bastard son shed lustre on the Howards and given the third duke's interests in heraldry and in commemorating his family, it would need explanation if Richmond's heraldry did *not* feature prominently on the tomb.

There are additional reasons to suppose that Richmond's tomb-chest was intended to feature heraldry, even though this part of the monument may not yet have been carved in 1539. Other components almost certainly intended for Richmond's tomb-chest survive. The two relief panels, showing bust-length figures of an Old Testament prophet and a king, discovered at Thetford in the nineteenth century and donated to the British Museum, have (as Marks showed) shell niches very similar to those on the third duke's tomb and their figure style is also consistent with it. Both panels have Roman numerals incised on their top surfaces (Fig. 46). These are assembly numbers, used by sculptors to indicate where the panels belonged in the tomb layout, to ensure they were put in the correct location when the monument was constructed. The fact that the panels are numbered suggests that carving of the whole series must have been very nearly finished, so the position of each individual panel could be finalised.[103] The fragment of a similar panel found in the 1930s excavations belongs with them, as noted above. Iconographically, these figures would be entirely consistent with the Old Testament narratives of Richmond's monument, which belong to the 1539 scheme.

If this hypothesis is correct, Richmond's tomb-chest was intended to be divided by architectural elements – half-shafts with bases and capitals – virtually identical to those of the third duke's tomb: at its corners the monument had baluster shafts, different from those of the third duke's monument but of the same scale and visually and iconographically related to them. On the sides of the tomb-chest, where the third duke's monument has apostles, Richmond's was intended to feature bust-length Old Testament figures placed over some other element, to bring the chest up to the same height. The fact that the figural panels in this section were bust-length only – as compared to the full-length images on the third duke's monument – must indicate that they stood above a non-figural element. As we have established, this missing layer was, very probably, heraldic. The reintroduction of heraldry into Richmond's monument by the fourth duke before it was erected in 1555 – if, as seems likely, the graffito indeed commemorates this – strikingly reasserted the link between the Tudors and the Howards. Perhaps, indeed, the third duke had been involved in its commissioning. The Old Testament narrative reliefs, still surviving today on Richmond's monument, would have stood above this lower tomb-chest. Other components excavated at Thetford assist us in envisaging the monument's originally intended appearance. The two angels holding shields with instruments of the Passion are survivors from a group intended to kneel on the tomb-chest. As we have seen above, Blomefield recorded what must have been an oral tradition that such figures belonged here. They go together with the four standing (wingless) figures

---

[103] The distinctive paper label with a blue border is that of Sir John Evans, the pioneering archaeologist (and father of Dame Joan Evans), who donated the panels to the British Museum from his huge collection of over 6,000 artefacts.

preserved at Framlingham at the corners of the tomb-chest. The latter images must originally have been intended to stand on top of the image-encrusted shafts planned for the corners of the monument, matching the position of the heraldic lions on the third duke's baluster shafts. Probably other elements associated with the heraldry assigned to Christ in the late Middle Ages (e.g. the Veronica and the face of a Jew, spitting) would have been painted on the four shields, not Richmond's heraldry. Richmond's tomb-chest would have been carved with an egg and dart – or more accurately egg and flower – moulding, a stylistic development of that on the third duke's monument. There, the foliate element is placed below the panelled upper section. On Richmond's monument, by contrast, it seems likely to have formed the upper termination.

A single New Testament relief, the Angel leading the three Magi, was discovered in the 1930s excavations. Chettle and the excavators assumed that it belonged to the same monument as all the other pieces. It does not. Almost certainly, whereas the other fragments belong to the Richmond monument, this relief belongs instead, as Marks suggested, with the third duke's monument. Where there are now plain panels, there was, in 1539, intended to be a series of New Testament reliefs, corresponding to those of the Old Testament on Richmond's monument. It can be proven that the relief was one of a series, even if no others have yet been discovered. After it had been excavated, the sides, top and bottom of the Magi relief had been clumsily covered with wet plaster and fitted into a wooden frame to hold it securely: the clunch has numerous hairline cracks, as can also be seen on the British Museum panels, and this treatment may have been precautionary. The plaster on the top was carefully removed for me by conservators, with the aim of revealing an assembly numeral on top of the panel. Painstaking work uncovered the number, VII (Fig. 47). Its existence proves that others in the series had also been carved and the places in which they were to be located on the monument had been determined. The New Testament narrative relief programme intended for the third duke's monument was abandoned rather than being recommissioned when work on erecting and completing the monument took place in the late 1550s. The graffito date – 1559 – may commemorate the end of work. Of course, the abandonment of this relief programme may simply have been an economy measure, but it could also indicate the relative lack of enthusiasm for commissioning narratives of Christ's life because of their potential contentiousness after the iconoclastic revolution of Edward VI's reign. The integration of the pre-Reformation Old Testament narratives into Richmond's monument and, more daringly, the placing of figures with shields of Christ's arms on its tomb-chest, doubtless belonged to Mary's reign, that monument being graffito dated 1555: under Elizabeth, the religious climate had abruptly changed again.

As we contemplate the monuments planned in 1539, we can grasp some of the third duke's objectives and how he intended the two monuments to work together, linked stylistically and iconographically. His own tomb-chest primarily featured New Testament subject matter: with apostles on the tomb-chest and a relief cycle of the nativity above (Fig. 48). However, Old Testament prophets were placed at the centre of the west and east ends and, on a small scale, on the baluster shafts. The heraldic focus was limited to the shield-holding lions on top of the baluster shafts – assuming that such figures were always intended to stand in the position they now occupy – and to the effigies and their ancillary decoration. The Duke of Richmond's monument exhibited his own and his Howard wife's heraldry on the tomb-chest surmounted by half-length Old Testament prophets, and with Old Testament narrative panels above (Fig. 49). The New Testament elements were confined to the kneeling angels holding Christ's coat of arms on the tomb-chest and standing atop the angled baluster shafts, flanking the effigies. The typological connecting of Old and New Testament themes, as seen in the contemporary stained glass at King's College Chapel, Cambridge where it is derived from *Biblia Pauperum* illustrations, is entirely characteristic of the period. Here, at Thetford in 1539, Old and New were to be subtly linked across the paired monuments, and the heraldic elements too were shared between them. There can be no doubt that from the first the monuments were conceived as a complementary pair, the formal and icono-graphic elements orchestrated in a visual counterpoint.

The monuments' iconography may give a clue as to where they were originally planned to stand within the priory church at Thetford. The fact that the narratives of Richmond's Old Testament reliefs open with the creation of Eve (Fig. 50) suggests that this intended location was the Lady Chapel of the Priory; for Mary was the new Eve, the instrument of man's redemption from the Fall caused by Eve. If, as seems probable, the upper section of the third duke's tomb-chest was intended to have a New Testament programme related to the nativity of Christ, this points in the same, Marian, direction. Pilgrims' donations to the priory's 'miraculous' image of the Virgin had funded the construction and enlargement of the substantial Lady Chapel at Thetford. It possessed architectural niches housing images of the Nativity of the Virgin and of her Assumption, whose subject matter the tomb reliefs would have supplemented. Howard interest in the building is shown by the fact that the duchess (presumably dowager duchess Agnes, not Elizabeth) had in 1529–30 given £1 towards the cost of ceiling of a two-storey chamber, probably a watching chamber to observe pilgrims accessing the chapel.[104] She had also donated other ornaments and jewels to the priory, perhaps connected with the chapel's

---

[104] Dymond (ed.), *Register*, I, 57 and II, 558, 691.

images.[105] The highly conservative religious beliefs of the monks, who had rescued the relic of St Philip's arm from Castle Acre Priory in 1537–8 after that priory's dissolution and given the relic a place in their own church, must have accorded with those of the duke.[106] Controversy over the worship of miracle-working images of the Virgin was extremely bitter in these years and the famous wooden statues from Walsingham and Ipswich were burnt at Chelsea in 1538 as part of the onslaught on superstitious imagery under Thomas Cromwell. So, if the third duke did select Thetford's Lady Chapel for his burial site, it could certainly have been construed as a profoundly reactionary choice.[107] Of course, purely practical considerations could also have determined his choice. The choir of the church was already flanked by Mowbray monuments and with the second Howard duke's tomb in the prime position, in front of the high altar, this area was full.[108]

Whatever his precise motivation, there are good reasons to believe that the third duke intended the two great new tombs being carved in 1539 to stand in the Lady Chapel, where they would also have been the focus of intercessory prayer.[109] In their present state and location, Richmond's and the third duke's monuments are remarkably important monuments, whose location, compromised appearance and unfinished condition reveal much about the religious changes of the mid-sixteenth century and about the problems faced by the third and fourth dukes. How much more imposing they would have been, had they been completed and installed in the church at Thetford as planned, to reveal to every observer the political power and religious beliefs, the family honour and the artistic taste of Thomas Howard, third Duke of Norfolk.

Acknowledgements

I am very grateful to Dr Lisa Ford, Dr Steven Gunn, Dr Meredith Hale and Professor Rosemary Sweet for their helpful improvements to a draft of this paper. Any errors which remain are my fault.

[105] Dymond (ed.), *Register*, II, 735.

[106] Dymond (ed.), *Register*, I, 56.

[107] J. Blatchly & D. MacCulloch, *Miracles in Lady Lane: the Ipswich Shrine at the Westgate*, Dorchester 2013; R. Deacon & P. Lindley, *Image and Idol: Medieval Sculpture*, London 2001, 32–3. For a conservative defence at the end of the previous decade, see T. M. C. Lawler, G. Marc'hadour & R. C. Marius (eds), *The Complete Works of St Thomas More*, Yale 1981, vol. 6, *A Dialogue Concerning Heresies*, of 1529.

[108] See Dr Hall's essay, above.

[109] P. Lindley, 'The Visual Arts and their Functions in the Pre-Reformation Church', in T. Hamling & R. L. Williams (eds), *Art Re-Formed; Re-assessing the Impact of the Reformation on the Visual Arts*, Newcastle 2007, 28–9.

The 1546 Declaration Regarding
the Arms at Thetford Priory

KIRSTEN CLAIDEN-YARDLEY

Henry Howard, earl of Surrey, and Thomas Howard, third duke of Norfolk were tried and found guilty of treason in January 1547. The indictment against Surrey stated that he had used the arms of Edward the Confessor with three silver labels. Edward the Confessor's arms were reserved for the King and the variation of the arms with silver labels was borne by the heir apparent, at this time Prince Edward. Surrey's use of the arms was interpreted as an act of treason on the grounds that he was assuming a false honour and, in the process, depriving the royal heir of marks of his honour.[1] Between Surrey's arrest in early December 1546 and his trial, Surrey was interrogated and evidence was collected from servants, friends, family members and heralds in order to determine the exact indictment he would face.[2] The property of both Surrey and his father was seized and inventories were taken of the goods at their properties, including Norfolk's house at Kenninghall and Mount Surrey – the earl of Surrey's house at St. Leonards, Norwich.[3] In addition, men were sent to Thetford Priory to report on the arms that they could see there. Their declaration has survived and provides a snapshot of the priory as it was seven years after its dissolution.[4] As there was a specific purpose to their visit, it is a partial picture that overlooks much that would be of interest to the modern historian or archaeologist. However, it does provide some clues as to the appearance of some tombs in the priory, the priory's state of repair in the decade following the Dissolution of the Monasteries, the strategy of the Howard family towards their tombs and the validity of the heraldic charges levelled against the Howards.

The majority of the document is given over to the description of the coats of arms carved on two tombs, one either side of the high altar. It does not give any indication of the dimensions and style of the tombs or whether they had effigies or epitaphs. The first of the two tombs is stated in the document to be that of one of the Mowbray dukes of Norfolk. Based on the heraldry, Thomas Martin identified this tomb as belonging to John Mowbray, third Mowbray duke

---

[1] W. A. Sessions, *Henry Howard the Poet Earl of Surrey: A Life*, Oxford 1999, 370.

[2] J. S. Brewer, J. Gairdner and R. H. Brodie, *Letters and Papers, Foreign and Domestic, of the Reign of Henry VIII: Preserved in the Public Record Office, the British Museum, and Elsewhere in England*, vol. 21, Pt 2, London 1910, 555.

[3] National Archives, LR2/115.

[4] National Archives, SP1/227 f. 128.

of Norfolk, who died in 1461.[5] The identification of the second tomb is more problematic. The declaration says 'th[er] is one Duke Thomas tom[m]e yt was kild at kings Rich feld a[s] it is said ther' and 'Rich feld' is generally interpreted as meaning the Battle of Bosworth. However, in that case an error has been made in the document as it was John Howard who died at Bosworth. On the basis of the described heraldry, Martin states that it is in fact the tomb of John Mowbray, fourth Mowbray duke of Norfolk, who died in 1476, and his wife, Elizabeth Talbot.[6] This is supported by John Weever's *Ancient Funerall Monuments*, compiled during the 1630s, which refers to the third and fourth Mowbray dukes of Norfolk having been entombed at Thetford Priory.[7] In reaching his conclusion, Martin identified two of the coats of arms on the tomb as being those of Talbot and Montgomery, earl of Shrewsbury. However, both those coats of arms have borders which are not mentioned in the declaration. Martin's identification is probably correct, given the supporting evidence from Weever, so some doubt has to be cast on the accuracy of the declaration.

It is clear that neither tomb belonged to the Howard family. Even allowing for slight mistakes in the description of the heraldry, there is no mention of the Howard family arms and the arms of marriage do not represent any of the marriages contracted by the Howard dukes. These two tombs were probably included in the declaration because of the prominence on them of the arms of England with three silver labels – the arms used by Thomas Brotherton, a younger son of Edward I. As this was a royal coat of arms in a Howard patronised property that had been sold to the third duke of Norfolk after the dissolution, it had the potential to be used as evidence against the Howards. However, the use of Brotherton's arms was granted to the Mowbray family by Richard II, along with the use of the crest that would have been used by the King's eldest son and the arms of Edward the Confessor. The Howards held their title as if the Mowbrays were their predecessors (despite inheriting it from the female line), and this was confirmed when Henry VIII restored the second Howard duke of Norfolk to his title.[8] Therefore the Mowbray arms were incorporated into the coat of arms borne by the Howards. We know from an illustration in the British Library that the second duke of Norfolk's tomb was covered with heraldry including Brotherton's arms[9] (Lindley, Fig. 13). If it had been standing in Thetford Priory in 1546, then surely it would have been

5   Thomas Martin, *The History of the Town of Thetford in the Counties of Norfolk and Suffolk, from the Earliest Accounts to the Present Time*, London 1779, 163.
6   Martin, *Thetford*, 164.
7   John Weever, *Antient Funeral Monuments of Great-Britain, Ireland and the Islands adjacent*, London 1767, 551.
8   Sessions, *Earl of Surrey*, 394.
9   British Library, Add. MS. 45131, f. 85.

included in the declaration. Its absence suggests that it had already been dismantled prior to December 1546. Also missing from the declaration is any mention of the tomb of Henry Fitzroy, duke of Richmond. As the illegitimate son of Henry VIII, his tomb naturally incorporates the arms of England and France. Its omission provides further support for the argument that the tombs of Fitzroy and the third duke of Norfolk were never erected at Thetford.

The declaration notes that a variation of Brotherton's arms with five labels was visible in 'very old painteur' on one of the roof arches, in a stained glass window and displayed next to a side altar. On the other side of the altar was an escutcheon bearing the arms of Edward the Confessor's father. Also noted was the escutcheon of the arms of England and France with three labels and a statue of a gentlewoman that stood on a tomb and held the arms of England and France with five labels. Rather than providing evidence to use against Thomas and Henry Howard, the inspection of the priory appears, if anything to justify the heraldry that they used. It provides clear evidence of the arms of Brotherton and other 'royal' arms being used by previous dukes of Norfolk. This must have bolstered the Howard family in thinking that they were also entitled to use those arms. However, they could have exercised more discretion, especially given Henry VIII's jealous protection of his royal rights. Faced with the political realities of the closing months of Henry VIII's reign, Thomas Howard, third duke of Norfolk would ultimately confess that, 'I have without authority borne in the first and principal quarter of my arms, ever since the death of my father, the arms of England with a difference of three labels of silver, which are the proper arms of my Lord the Prince'.[10]

An unintended consequence of this declaration is that, whilst there is much that it does not describe, it does give some clues as to Howard's attitudes towards the priory after its dissolution. That stained glass windows and roof arches were intact supports the view that the Howards were concerned with preserving the priory rather than dismantling it or converting it to domestic use. We also get a glimpse of tombs that have now been lost. Finally, we also learn that whilst the Howards were proud of their Mowbray ancestry and made use of their inherited heraldry, that pride had not suggested the removal of their Mowbray predecessors' tombs from the dissolved priory in order to preserve them.

[10]   Brewer, Gairdner and Brodie, *Letters and Papers*, vol. 21, Pt 2, 696.

APPENDIX:

TRANSCRIPTION of SP 1/227 f. 128 (Dec. 1546)

Kirsten Claiden-Yardley

A brieff declaracion of the armes th[a]t we// hav [*seen*] in the late abbey of Thetford

In p[rim]is at the first aulter standing at the upper end of the// body of the Church on the lefte side of the same th[er] is in a// scouchin by it self Broth[er]tons arm[es] w[ith] five Labell[es] & on the// right side of the said aulte is ther in a scouchin by it self// the armes of England & Fraunce quarterd togither w[ith]a silv[er]// labell of iij points powderd & fast by the same in a noth[er] sco[*uchin*]// Seint Edward[es] fath[eres] arm[es] th[a]t is to say a crosse flowry w[ith] iiij// martlett[es] It[em] entring into thesaid abbey on the lefte side of the [*same*]// in a glasse window is Broth[er]tons arm[es] w[ith] v labell[es] It[em]// entring into the queare on the furdest arche of the rouffe of the// body of thesaid church is painted in very old painteur in [...]// soundry scouchins Broth[er]tons arm[es] w[ith] v labell[es] so th[a]t in all// the church as far as we culd see ther wer no lyons w[ith]// iij labelles saving apon these iij tumm[es] heraft[er] exp[re]ssed

It[em] on the lefte side of the queare going up to the high aulte// is Moubrays tomne so[m]tyme Duke of Norff which is [...]// w[ith] div[ers] scouchins the one is the arm[es] of England w[ith] v [*labelles*]// a noth[er] the arm[es] of England w[ith] iij labell[es] a noth[er] scochin// divided in the middyst wh[cr]of the one halff is tharm[es] of England [*with*]// iij labell[es] of silv[er] & the oth[er] halff quarterd w[ith] ij soundry Cot[es] ye first// silv[er] w[ith] a crosse raggid of Gul[es] & [*iiij*] of these signs [sketch of a waterbouget] in sabu[*lle*]// of ev[er]y side of the crosse the oth[er] Cote Gul[es] w[ith] a barr of silv[er]// w[ith] ix of these [sketch of a billet] in gold iij above the barr & vj beneth It[em] a [*nother*]// scouchin by himselff the full armes of England & Fraunce q[ua]rterd// saving th[a]t in ye neth[er] quarter [*wher*] the arm[es] of fraunce shold be// he bear[es] asur w[ith] a barre of silv[er] slopewise [...]// rampant of gold th[a]t is [...] say [...] on the one side of [...]// iij on the other

It[em] on the Right side of the queare as [*we*] go up to the high ault[er]// th[er] is one Duke Thom[a]s Tom[m]e th[a]t was kild at king[es] Rich feld [*as*]// it is said ther wich is garnisshed w[ith] div[ers] scouchins the one// is the arm[es] of england w[ith] iij silv[er] labell[es] It[em] in a noth[er]// scouchin the one halff of it is the Cote of england w[ith]// iij silv[er][*labelles*] & in the oth[er] halff these soundry Cot[es] th[a]t// is to say the one of those Cot[es] the feld Gules & a lyon// of gold rampant the next Cote is asur a lyon of gold// [r]ampant the thirde is Gul[es] w[ith] a barr of gold gardid w[ith]// ij [...] of sabull[es] & vj apati crosses of gold iij above the barr// & iij benethe the iiijth Cote is silv[er] & ij lyons currant or// passant of Gul[es] the vth Cote is Gul[es] w[ith] a lyon of// silver regardant crowned w[ith] a Coron of gold It[em] ye vjth// Cote is chekkerd w[ith] gold & asur w[ith] a chevern of silver// powderd & hemyd in w[ith] blak [?listes] It[em] th[er] is a noth[er] scouchin// apon thesaid Tu[mme] th[a]t bear[es] a partid feld of gold & vert// w[ith] a lyon rampant of G[ules] & it is to be noted th[a]t apon// th[a]t tomne th[er] is no arm[es[of england w[ith] v labell[es] but// only w[ith] iij saving the litle gentle woman th[a]t stand[es] apo[n]// the Tom[m]e w[hich] bear[es] the said arm[es] of england & fraunce// w[ith] v labell[es]

A brief declarac[i]on of// the arms seen in thabbey// of Thetford

Editor's Key:
// indicate ends of lines.
thorn modernised to 'th' so 'the' rather than 'ye'.
[text in square brackets] used for expanded abbreviations.
[*word in italics*] for where a word is faded or damaged but I have deduced what it probably was.
[...] for where a section of text is lost or faded and I do not know what the word was or it is impossible to tell if multiple words are lost.
[?word] for where the ink is visible but I am not totally confident in the letters or word I have transcribed.
The original text contains no punctuation and none has been inserted in the edition.

The Missing Link? The Duke of Norfolk's Travels and French Renaissance Tomb Sculpture

REBECCA CONSTABEL

The tomb-monument of the third Howard duke of Norfolk at Framlingham, Suffolk, is undoubtedly a remarkable monument (Fig. 1). In England, there are few tombs comparable in terms of its craftsmanship or overall construction. Twelve figures of apostles and two Old Testament prophets, standing underneath distinctive shell-headed niches line the sides and ends of the tomb chest, a design uncommon in sixteenth-century England. Based upon the style and iconography of Howard's tomb, it has therefore been suggested that it either has foreign roots or that it draws upon foreign influences for its composition, if not for its execution.[1] Documentary evidence, however, is either scarce or inconclusive, making it necessary to use other means of investigation.

Visual and physical examinations of the monument can provide first results. Although uncommon in England, the twelve figures of apostles underneath shell-headed niches resemble a design commonly found throughout sixteenth-century France: most notably on the monument of Francis II of Brittany (d. 1488) and his wife at Nantes, finished in 1507 (Fig. 2); the sepulchre of the dukes of Orleans at Saint-Denis, completed in 1504 (Fig. 3); or the tomb of Artus Gouffier (d. 1519), installed in the church of Saint-Maurice at Oiron by 1540 (Fig. 4). On this basis it has been argued that the third duke's tomb at Framlingham may be by French sculptors, or at least be French-inspired.[2] Given that we know that the duke of Norfolk was the patron of the monument, it seems essential to explore his visits to France to determine when he could have had the opportunity to see French tombs for himself, and so to determine whether he himself selected specific models for his own monument. Norfolk embarked on a number of visits to France; most, however, were either military campaigns or only short-term, such as the military campaigns of Morlaix and Doullens in 1522. The most extended, and thus perhaps the most promising, are Norfolk's three-month long travels in 1533, some six years before we know his monument and that of

---

[1] Lawrence Stone and Howard Colvin, 'The Howard tombs at Framlingham, Suffolk', *Archaeological Journal*, 122 (1965), 159–71; Richard Marks, 'The Howard Tombs at Thetford and Framlingham: New Discoveries', *Archaeological Journal*, 141 (1984), 252–67.

[2] Stone & Colvin, 168–9, in particular, point towards shared architectural elements with the court of Francis I, such as elaborate pillars, shell niches and baluster shafts; Marks, 259, 263, also pointed towards the significance of the Old Testament scenes and shell niches.

Richmond were under construction.[3]

In the summer of 1533, the third duke of Norfolk embarked on a diplomatic mission to France. The purpose of this journey was for Norfolk to meet Pope Clement VII, in order to persuade him to revoke his threat to excommunicate Henry VIII if the king refused to take Katherine of Aragon back as his wife by September.[4] Thanks to a variety of sources, such as letters and other official correspondence, it has been possible to reconstruct the key points of Norfolk's route through France.[5] Setting off across the channel in late May, Norfolk was reportedly in Calais on 30 May and remained there until at least 2 June, before setting out to Paris[6] By 12 June, if not earlier, he had arrived in Paris, where the party remained until 18 June.[7] Norfolk planned to leave for Lyons on 19 June.[8] He travelled south via Montargis, visiting Melun and the basilica of Saint-Mathurin along the route.[9] On 23 June, Norfolk stayed in Briare, planning to arrive at Le Puy, his rendezvous point with the French king Francis I, on 2 July.[10] Due to a series of delays, the date and the location of their meeting were soon changed. According to a letter from one of Norfolk's travelling companions written in Moulins on 28 June, the duke now planned to meet Francis I at Riom.[11] The two men were then to progress to Le Puy together.[12] As part of this plan, a guide would be despatched to arrive on 28 or 29 June; he would then accompany Norfolk to the meeting point. Other letters mention the key stopover points along the pilgrimage route leading south, including La-Charité-sur-Loire, Nevers and Moulins.[13] The party arrived at Riom

3   James Gairdner (ed.), *Letters and Papers, Foreign and Domestic, of the Reign of Henry VIII: VI, 1533* (London, 1882), 558 [hereafter *L&P*].

4   Francis had organised a meeting with the pope, partly at Henry's urging, and partly for his own business. Norfolk acted as an ambassador in this matter. One of Norfolk's tasks was to persuade Francis to intercede with the pope on Henry's behalf at their scheduled meeting, while equally preventing the French monarch from arranging a marriage between his son Henri and Catherine de Medici, the pope's niece. However, as time progressed Norfolk's orders were more complex than this, and Henry frequently revised his instructions to the duke. See R. J. Knecht, *Francis I*, Cambridge 1982, 225–8. See Geoffrey de C. Parmiter, *The King's Great Matter: A study of Anglo-Papal Relations 1527–1534*, London 1967, 244–52, for a more detailed summary of the complexities of Norfolk's journey.

5   In the reconstruction of Norfolk's route, *L&P* has been most helpful.

6   *L&P*, 558; 587.

7   *L&P*, 631; 669.

8   *L&P*, 669. In this letter, Peter Vannes wrote to Lord Cromwell that they were uncertain if Francis was at Lyons or Avignon on his progress through southern France.

9   *L&P*, 831.

10   *L&P*, 687.

11   *L&P*, 718.

12   Ibid.

in the first week of July. In a letter from 12 July, we learn that Norfolk had met the French king just outside the town on 10 July.[14] The duke had spent some time with the king before Francis carried on to Clermont, while he himself stayed at Montferrand.[15] Norfolk remained there for the following days, as the duke had progressed to Courpière by 15 July.[16] In a letter written by Francis the next day, we learn that Norfolk had been with him at Clermont for the previous four or five days, but as he had fallen ill, he had been sent to Lyons, a major communication hub in the sixteenth century, to recover.[17] Since Norfolk was awaiting a letter from Clement about their future meeting, it seemed prudent to send him to a location where messengers could reach him more easily. Norfolk arrived in Lyons by 21 July.[18] On 24 July he dined at Grézieu-la-Varenne, although he returned to Lyons afterwards.[19]

After much postponing of the meeting, Norfolk's travels in France soon came to an abrupt end in August, when Clement finally refused to meet the duke after all.[20] In late July or early August – it is unclear precisely when – Norfolk had travelled from Lyons to Montpellier.[21] A letter from Francis I indicates that Norfolk had complained to him at Montpellier about the pope's decision, while insisting on the execution of Henry's orders to return home immediately should there be no settlement.[22] This turn of events is reflected in the haste evident in Norfolk's actions to return to England, which implies that in contrast to his outward journey, he had little time to visit churches along his route home. In a letter from 14 August, it is suggested for the first time that Norfolk had been ordered to return to England.[23] Further letters echo this. A letter dated 24 August confirms that Norfolk was on his way back and that he planned to be in Calais by 30 August.[24] On this basis, it would imply a travelling rate of 1090 km within

---

[13]   *L&P*, 831.

[14]   *L&P*, 811.

[15]   The modern city of Clermont-Ferrand consisted of separate towns in the sixteenth century.

[16]   *L&P*, 830; 831.

[17]   Francis I to Bailly of Troyes, see *LP*, 846.

[18]   *L&P*, 891.

[19]   Ibid.

[20]   For the scheduling and re-scheduling of the meeting, see *L&P*, 631, 642, 979, 1038.

[21]   In a letter written on 12 August, Francis wrote that Norfolk had left Lyons, presumably some time before 12 August, and that he had not yet reached Francis at the time of writing. *L&P*, 973. Unfortunately, this means a gap in the reconstruction of Norfolk's route and location.

[22]   *L&P*, 1038. As an indication of Norfolk's haste, he wrote to Lord Lisle before reaching Calais, 'My going to the king requires such diligence that I cannot remain with you half an hour if wind and tide may serve'. *L&P*, 1042. On Henry's last instructions to Norfolk before his return, see also *L&P*, 954.

[23]   *L&P*, 979; 980.

sixteen days, making for a realistic, yet by no means slow, average long-distance travelling pace of 68km per day.[25] In a letter from Francis to his bailey of Troyes from 27 August he also confirmed that Norfolk was on his way home, and that he was presumably already north at this point.[26] Francis' estimate was correct. In a letter written at 3pm on 28 August, Norfolk had reached the northern French town of Amiens, suggesting that his timing was tighter than originally planned if he wanted to embark for England on 30 August.[27] By the evening of 28 August, he therefore aimed to arrive at Abbeville, 50 km further on.[28] Sending an envoy ahead to Lord Lisle in Calais, he ordered replacement horses to be ready at 'Marguison' for 10am the next morning.[29] It can be safely presumed that Marguison corresponds to the modern town of Marquise, which is a further 90km down the road from Abbeville, but only about 25km from Calais.[30] For the final part of the journey through France, these last letters suggest a travelling pace of at least 140km within less than 24hours – a remarkable feat in terms of a rider's stamina and logistics![31] The gruelling pace in the final stages of the journey, however, paid off. On 30 August, he embarked at Calais as planned, to return to London within the day.

Norfolk's journey in 1533 suggests a possible route to investigate the French influences – or lack thereof – on his own monuments. The key questions are if, and if so, to what extent, the monuments he may have seen on his travels influenced his sepulchral commissions six years later. Unfortunately, it is extremely difficult to reconstruct exactly which monuments Norfolk may have visited in France. A large proportion of tomb sculpture in France has been accidentally or deliberately damaged, if not completely destroyed, during the course of the Wars of Religion, the French Revolution and the wars of the nineteenth and twentieth centuries.[32] The effects of the turbulent times are

[24]   *L&P*, 1030. The letter was addressed to Lord Lisle in Calais.
[25]   This estimate is based upon a return journey from Montpellier to Calais, presumably following the route via Le Puy, Clermont-Ferrand, Moulins, Briare, as well as incorporating the known stops Amiens, Abbeville, and Marquise. Suggesting a gross riding time of less than six hours at a steady trot of 12km per hour, this pace seems adequate given Henry's orders for Norfolk to return without delay, yet it is not high enough to cause lasting damage to the horses.
[26]   *L&P*, 1038.
[27]   *L&P*, 1042.
[28]   Ibid.
[29]   Ibid.
[30]   Henry VIII made his camp there during his invasion of France in the summer of 1544, as shown in one of the murals at Cowdray House (now destroyed).
[31]   Given Norfolk's average travelling pace of almost 70km per day, this effectively means he was only one day behind schedule.
[32]   Kurt Bauch, *Das mittelalterliche Grabbild: figürliche Grabmäler des 11. bis 15. Jahrhunderts in Europa,* New York 1976, 6. See also Elizabeth Brown, 'The Oxford

particularly disastrous along Norfolk's route south. Although some of the key churches mentioned in the correspondence above still exist today, the majority have suffered severely over the centuries, either during the Wars of Religion, or again during the French Revolution, when the monarchy and the nobility were equally under attack.[33] The buildings and sculptures which survived both episodes, in turn frequently fell victim to fires, or the bombings of the World Wars. Consequently, very few churches which Norfolk may have visited in 1533 remain intact until today, making it difficult to reconstruct precisely which monuments he may have encountered on his travels. To name just a small selection of the churches, the former key pilgrimage site of La-Charité-sur Loire today consists mostly of modern additions to historic buildings constructed after the devastating fire of 1559, which destroyed most of the church as well as most of the town. The convent of Saint-Mathurin, formerly a formidable basilica about 20km south of Fontainebleau, was severely damaged during the Wars of Religion and today only consists of inaccessible ruins.[34]

Nevertheless, a choice selection of monuments along Norfolk's route (Fig. 6) has survived the deliberate or accidental mutilation and destruction of the previous centuries. The Bourbon family mausoleum in the priory of Souvigny is one of the most significant fifteenth-century burial sites.[35] It is also remarkably close to a recorded stopping point on Norfolk's route. As recorded in the letter from 15 July 1533, Norfolk stayed at the castle of Moulins at the heart of the Bourbonnais.[36] It would not be surprising if Norfolk had visited the Bourbon family mausoleum at the priory of Souvigny, situated at less than an hour's ride from Moulins.[37] The source material on Norfolk's time in the Bourbonnais is also particularly curious. It specifically mentions that Norfolk had stayed at the former house of the connétable de Bourbon at Moulins, who had previously forfeited his rights and titles after committing treason.[38] This mention of his

---

Collection of the Drawings of Roger de Gaignières and the Royal Tombs of Saint-Denis', *Transactions of the American Philosophical Society* 78 (1988), 6–7, as an example of the destruction of the royal tombs at Saint-Denis during the French Revolution.

[33] This often resulted in figures of saints on tomb monuments being mistaken for kings, which were thus ritually beheaded. See Francis Haskell, *History and its Images: Art and Interpretation of the Past*, New Haven 1993, 137.

[34] The Gaignières drawings, for instance, do not include monuments from this church.

[35] Arthur Gardner, *Medieval Figure Sculpture in France*, Cambridge 1931, 477. See Antje-Fee Köllermann, 'Das Grabmal von Louis II de Bourbon und Anne d'Auvergne', *Wiener Jahrbuch für Kunstgeschichte*, 51 (2000), 33–62.

[36] *L&P*, 831. The two towns are 10km apart.

[37] Gardner, *Medieval figure sculpture in France*, 477. See Köllermann, 'Das Grabmal von Louis II de Bourbon', 33–62.

[38] He died leading a fatal attack on Saint Peter's in Rome in 1527. The letter was written

residence is unique in all the letters from Norfolk's journey, as the other documents only mention dinners with French nobles or the overall locality of his stay, yet never the actual residence.[39] While the monuments themselves do not bear much resemblance to Norfolk's tombs other than in size, perhaps this specific mention suggests that the Bourbon heartland made a greater impression on Norfolk and his entourage than the surviving letters indicate.

Further away from Norfolk's immediate route, however, a significant selection of funerary monuments in France still survives today and some of these, rather than the monuments along his route, have been linked to the Framlingham tombs. The most famous of the surviving monuments are undoubtedly the tomb of Louis XII (d. 1515) and Anne of Brittany (d. 1514), featuring twelve apostles; and the monument of the dukes of Orleans (d. 1407, 1408, 1420, 1465) (Fig. 3), featuring twenty-four figures of apostles and saints underneath shell-headed niches; both now at Saint-Denis. The tomb of Louis XII was finished at Saint-Denis in 1531, while the monument of the dukes of Orleans had been situated at the Célestins in Paris for almost thirty years during Norfolk's travels in 1533. Outside of Paris, the tomb monument of Anne of Brittany's parents, Francis II of Brittany (d. 1488) and his wife Marguerite, at Nantes must also be mentioned in the context of Norfolk's tomb.[40] Although situated at the opposite end of the country to Norfolk's route, one could perhaps draw stylistic and iconographical parallels between the figures of apostles on this monument and those at Framlingham.[41] Two further monuments, equally located significant distances from Norfolk's route, are the tomb of Artus Gouffier at Oiron, already mentioned above; and the monument of Imbert de Batarnay at Montrésor, presumably constructed between 1520 and 1530 (Fig. 5).[42] The latter features three effigies upon a square tomb chest lined with twelve apostles underneath prominent shell niches. The four corners of the monument display angels holding the deceased couple's coats-of-arms, similar to the lions placed at the four corners of the third duke's monument at Framlingham.[43] The last, and perhaps the most puzzling, link may be an alabaster tomb formerly at the Montmorency family residence at Écouen, near Paris, where Norfolk spent considerable amounts of time on his travels. This rather striking Italian Renaissance style

---

by one of Norfolk's travelling companions and addressed to Lord Cromwell. See *L&P*, 831.

[39] See *L&P*, 831.

[40] It was installed in 1507.

[41] Small figures of mourners are situated underneath shell niches, and twelve apostles line the tomb chest. See Anthony Blunt, *Art and Architecture in France 1500–1700*, Harmondsworth 1980, 40–1.

[42] Marks, 263 ; Paul Vitry, *Michel Colombe et la sculpture française de son temps*, Paris 1901, 144–5, 459.

[43] Stone & Colvin, 169.

monument also displays shell niches and putti heads, but it uses virtues rather than figures of apostles underneath the shell niches.[44] Datable to the late fifteenth or early sixteenth century, this is the first potentially geographically and stylistically significant monument which may have influenced Norfolk. As Anne de Montmorency was a prominent French nobleman and also part of the envoy meeting with Clement VII at Marseille in the autumn of 1533, it is highly likely that Norfolk would have seen this tomb in 1533.[45] Unfortunately, however, there is little more than circumstantial evidence to support the suggestion that these monuments, and in particular the Écouen tomb, impacted on Norfolk's choice of sepulchres for Thetford/Framlingham.

Fascinatingly, there are, however, some more peculiarities of the Framlingham tomb monuments which are also found on funerary monuments in France. Part of the dating evidence for the Howard tombs at Framlingham has rested on two graffito inscriptions found on the third duke's and Richmond's tombs.[46] On the bottom edge of the top south-western panel of the third duke's funerary monument, the date '1559' has been inscribed (Fig. 7). On Richmond's tomb, the date '1555' is etched on the east end of the monument (Fig. 8). Both are small and difficult to find unless one is looking for them specifically. The date 1559 is merely one centimetre in height at the highest point, while 1555 is approximately two and a half centimetres tall. Lawrence Stone and Howard Colvin have argued that these dates are contemporary to the tomb monument, although they were less certain whether the dates refer to the construction or the erection of the monuments within the church.[47] The dates are clearly not part of an official epitaph or inscription, and therefore it is worth investigating their specific role here, as well as establishing if similar inscriptions exist on tomb monuments elsewhere.

Stone and Colvin suggested that the dates were 'contemporary, to judge from the character of the Arabic figures', yet they did not investigate this suggestion further.[48] It is therefore worth examining the dates palaeographically before turning to comparisons with French material. Palaeography, the study of handwriting, often proves useful in establishing the origin of a written sample. At Framlingham, both dates are inscribed in similar depths to the masons' marks also found on the monuments. In the case of the date 1555, it is situated just above a mason's mark. There are several observations to be made regarding the

---

[44] Réunion des musées nationaux, [http://www.photo.rmn.fr/c/htm/CPicZ.aspx?E=I_2C6NU0PYC7BZ&o=THT], accessed 28 June 2013.

[45] Thierry Rentet, 'Anne de Montmorency (1493–1567). Le conseiller médiocre', in Cédric Michon (ed.), *Les conseillers de François Ier*, Rennes 2011, 301.

[46] Stone & Colvin, 166.

[47] Stone & Colvin, 166.

[48] Stone & Colvin, 166.

size, shape and conduct of the inscribed dates. Both dates are conducted in what may be described as an Italic hand, although the hands themselves are different. The number 5s on Richmond's tomb are consecutively S-shaped, while the 1 resembles the capital I. The fluidity in which this date is inscribed is remarkable, particularly if compared to the superficial, at times shaky hands which produce true graffiti found on some of the other monuments within the church. The etching gives the impression of being the skilled strokes of a person used to working in stone, rather than the superficial and sometimes illegible scratches on the surface as on the south-eastern panels of the third duke's tomb (Fig. 9). This depth suggests that the person who etched them knew the material and was skilled at working with it. However, the date scratched on the third duke's tomb is even more remarkable, in that it is produced in an extremely neat and tidy hand. More so than the date on Richmond's tomb, the incision could have easily been produced in the context of court correspondence, so extraordinary is the quality and neatness of the hand.

As the script employed for both dates is Italic, some deductions can be made as to skills, and perhaps even the identity, of its producer. Italic became popular in the course of the sixteenth century as the most significant script used in courtly correspondence. It required a certain amount of education, although it is renowned for its comparative ease and fluidity in the learning process. For this reason it was deemed a suitable script to teach to ladies, but it was also favoured by humanists. Therefore the Italic hand, particularly on the third duke's tomb, indicates that the writer appeared to have had a humanist education, in addition to his obvious skill in working stone which enabled him to produce such a high-quality inscription.

In terms of the nationality of the scribe, however, matters are more complex. In general terms, it is possible to identify the national origin of handwriting, as it is most frequently done with illuminated manuscripts. In contrast to the illustrations on medieval manuscripts, it is undoubtedly difficult to ascertain the national origin of a hand on the basis of four digits alone. However, due to the manuscript-like appearance of the inscribed date, it is perhaps possible to compare the overall appearance to handwritten samples from the time. The hand who wrote 1559 uses a formal, highly ligatured version of Italic; the most notable elements being the long, down-ward sloping strokes at the bottom of the 5s and the 9. This form of Italic is rare at the mid-sixteenth-century English court; nor does it become common in Cambridge before the 1570s.[49] The hand here is clearly not one of Roger Ascham's disciples, who

---

[49] Alfred J. Fairbank, *The Italic Hand in Tudor Cambridge: Forty-One Examples*, London, 1962. See also Alfred Fairbank and Berthold Wolpe, *Renaissance Handwriting: an Anthology of Italic Scripts*, London 1960.

characteristically produced rather spidery hands in his students, most famously the later Queen Elizabeth I, nor does it seem to belong to the male members of the Howard family, who produced hands closer to diplomatic than Italic.[50] Comparison with the handwriting of other key figures at the English court, from kings and queens, to secretaries and other noblemen, does not produce matches either. On this basis, it seems highly unlikely, but by no means impossible, that the person who wrote the inscription learned to write in England.

If England fails to produce a close match, however, it is worth expanding the search abroad. By comparing the date 1559 to samples from the court of Francis I, we face the same dilemma: it appears that most courtiers favoured a quicker and more practical script in their correspondence, such as diplomatic. It is therefore possible to narrow the potential influences on this date down even further. The elongated ligatures of the date are characteristic of a variation of Italic termed chancery script, which is a speedier version of Italic, developed at the papal court, and still in use in the 1550s and 1560s[51] Chancery was taught by two key writing masters in the first half of the sixteenth-century: Ludovico degli Arrighi and Giovanantonio Tagliente.[52] Arrighi is most famous for his *La Operina*, a treatise on how to write chancery script, first published in 1522 and reprinted in 1533. Tagliente also produced a number of handwriting manuals throughout the 1520s and 1530s. The first of these was published in 1524 and proved highly popular on the continent, undergoing a minimum of thirty-five editions.[53] Tagliente had a specific interest in teaching chancery to a commercial audience, thus making commercial correspondence the key focus of his exercises.[54] The appeal of his teachings to a commercial audience as well as the characteristic ligatures on the Framlingham date matching Arrighi's work make it highly attractive to speculate that, although perhaps not Italian himself, the man producing the date must have had access to Italian handwriting manuscripts

[50] Giles Edwin Dawson, *Elizabethan Handwriting 1500–1650 : a Guide to the Readings and documents and manuscripts*, London 1968.

[51] Dorothy E. Miner, Victor I. Carlson and P. W. Filby (eds), *2000 Years of Calligraphy: a Three-Part Exhibition Organized by the Baltimore Museum of Art, the Peabody Institute Library and the Walters Art Gallery*, Baltimore 1972, 79.

[52] Both men were influential tutors of scribes in the first quarter of sixteenth-century Italy. See *2000 Years of Calligraphy*, 80; and Stanley Morison, *Politics and Script: Aspects of Authority and Freedom in the Development of Graeco-Latin Script from the Sixth Century B. C. to the Twentieth A. D.*, Oxford 1972, 302.

[53] Anne Jacobsen Schutte, 'Teaching Adults to Read in Sixteenth-Century Venice: Giovanni Antonio Tagliente's *Libro Maistrevole*', *Sixteenth Century Journal*, 17 (1986), 6; also Herbert C. Schulz, 'The Teaching of Handwriting in Tudor and Stuart Times', *Huntingdon Library Quarterly* 6 (1943), 412; and Armando Petrucci, 'Pouvoir de l'écriture, pouvoir sur l'écriture de la Renaissance italienne', *Annales. Histoire, Sciences Sociales*, 43 (1988), 839.

[54] Schutte, 'Teaching adults', 13–14.

of the 1520s and 1530s.[55] This palaeographic dating, however, still works in conjunction with the theory of a two-phase monument, as it is evident that the inscriptions belonged to the later phase. Although one should exert a certain amount of caution since this statement is based upon little more evidence than four digits, the palaeographical analysis of the dates on the tombs, particularly on the third duke's tomb, at least supports the theory that one of the sculptors was foreign.

Despite the Italianate appearance of the handwriting on the third duke's tomb, a variety of French tomb monuments equally show the peculiar inscriptions outside the official epitaph. It is to these specimens that we may turn for help regarding the Framlingham tombs. The most notable cases are on the tombs of Raoul de Lannoy at Folleville, Artus Gouffier at Oiron, Jacques d'Estouteville at Valmont and Bishop Thomas James at Dol-de-Bretagne. In all cases, the additional inscriptions occur outside of the official epitaph. One of the easiest to read and best-documented inscriptions is situated on the foot end of the tomb of Raoul de Lannoy (d. 1508) and his wife Jehanne de Poix (d. 1524) at Folleville (Fig. 10).[56] Two small inscriptions at the feet of the effigies name the Italian sculptor Antonio della Porta as the artist responsible for the construction of the monument. The Roman capital letters beneath Raoul's feet read 'ANTONIUS PORTA/ TAMAGNINUS MEDIOLANENSIS FACIEBAT' (Fig. 11).[57] The more eroded inscription beneath the feet of the lady provides the same information in slightly different wording: 'ANTONIO/ TAMAGNINO/ DE MILANO/ FACIEB[AT]'. Instead of the round-hand letters used for the official epitaph, the information regarding the sculptor is deliberately set apart from the identity of the deceased, and is comparable to an artist's signature on a painting.[58]

The tomb of Artus Gouffier (d. 1519) at Oiron is another example of an inscription separate from the existing epitaph (Fig. 4). The tomb was constructed between 1510 and 1540.[59] Underneath the actual epitaph weaving around the

[55] This does however not necessarily imply that the graffiti were written in the 1530s, merely that the inscriber learnt to write in the 1520s or 1530s. Twenty years later in the 1550s he would have been old enough to be the master sculptor himself.
[56] For an old, but still the most thorough, work on this monument, see Georges Durand, 'Les Lannoy, Folleville, et l'art italien dans le nord de la France', *Bulletin Monumental*, 70 (1906), 329–404. For more recent work, see Christine Debrie, 'Les monuments sculptes du chœur de l'église de Folleville : XVIᵉ siècle', *Revue du Nord* 63 (1981), 415–38.
[57] The second row is slightly more tilted towards the right than the first row.
[58] See also Susie Nash, *Northern Renaissance Art*, Oxford 2008, 143–56, on authorship and dates etched into sculpture.
[59] Jean Guillaume, 'Les tombes des Gouffier: dieul familial et piété personnelle au milieu du XVIe siècle', in Jean Balsamo (ed.), *Les funérailles à la Renaissance*, Geneva 2002, 131–40, for an introduction to both monuments.

top of the slab, there is a small date inscribed in the stone. Depending on the bottom strokes of the last two digits which are now illegible, it is either 1522 or 1533 (Fig. 12). Similarly to the third duke's tomb at Framlingham, the date itself appears to be conducted in an Italic hand, which makes it a contemporary script to the construction of the tomb. Unfortunately it is too erased to produce any further accurate analysis of its origins. Yet since the date itself coincides with the construction of the monument, this again suggests that it too does not constitute graffiti, but that it has a connection with the sculptor. In a similar manner, the tomb of Philippe de Montmorency (d. 1516), in the same church, may have also had a date, beginning with 1 and ending in 6, inscribed just below the beginning of the actual epitaph; again, it is now too erased to read without specialist equipment. Comparable to the tomb at Folleville, both tombs were at least partially constructed by the Italian sculptor Giovanni Giusti (1485–1549) who settled in France, although his participation in the work on the monuments in the 1530s occurred after the initial work had already begun.

These are not the only examples, however. On the tomb of Jacques d'Estouteville (1448–89) and his wife Louise d'Albret (d. 1494) at Valmont, there appears to be another date, 1518, inscribed on the misaligned north panel of the west face of the monument. According to official records, the tomb was erected in the church in 1518, suggesting that the date marks the occasion. Despite these parallels, this tomb is slightly less straight-forward than the previous examples. On the one hand, it has been severely damaged and reconstructed in a different order. Since the panel it is inscribed upon does not fit the other two panels on this side, it can be presumed that the dated panel once belonged to the opposite side of the monument. Furthermore, the Estouteville tomb is a two-phase monument, consisting of a distinct late Gothic and a distinct early Renaissance phase, suggesting that the date 1518 belongs to the later construction period.

Finally, the tomb of Bishop Thomas James at Dol-de-Bretagne, also features what has been read as '1496', although in its current state it is closer to 1506, which would once again place the inscribed date right into the heart of the construction period of the tomb (Fig. 13).[60] As this monument was reportedly finished by the same Giusti in 1507 as the sculptors who finished the monuments at Oiron, this date would once again point towards a direct correlation between

---

[60] For introductions to this monument, see A. Rhein, 'La cathédrale de Dol', *Bulletin monumental* 74 (1910), 369–433; and Xenia Muratova, 'The Tomb of Bishop Thomas James in the Cathedral of Dol: a Monument of the Early Italian Renaissance Influence in Gothic Brittany', in John Mitchell (ed.), *England and the Continent in the Middle Ages: Studies in Memory of Andrew Martindale. Proceedings of the 1996 Harlaxton Symposium,* Stamford 2000, pp. 349–64.

the inscribed date and the construction of the tomb.[61] More significant than the date, however, is the sculptor's inscription on the west column of the monument. On the base of the left outside pilaster, the sculptor's inscription appears in Gothic letters: 'Scelte struxit opus magister istud/ Johes cuius cognomen est Justus/ et florentini[us]', informing the reader that this is the work of a Florentine named Johannes Justus, in other words, Giovanni Giusti (Fig. 14). This inscription specifically identifies the monument as the work of Giovanni Giusti, therefore creating a direct connection with the sculptor and contemporary inscriptions outside of the official epitaph.

How does all this help in assessing possible foreign influences on Norfolk's tomb at Framlingham? Following the French pattern which links informal inscriptions on tombs with the sculptor, this short survey indicates that the sculptors of Norfolk's tomb monument were probably not English. Establishing their actual national origins, however, is more difficult. Investigation of Norfolk's diplomatic mission in 1533 and some of the details on his tomb have successfully pointed to France. A series of cross-over points have emerged from this investigation. The peculiar date inscribed on his own tomb at Framlingham shows strong similarities to dates equally found on Renaissance monuments in France. In all five cases, the dates on the French tombs appear to stand in direct correlation with the construction and the sculptor of the monuments. However, equally in all cases, at least one of the key sculptors employed in working the French tombs was either of Italian origin or had learned his trade in Italy before working in France. On this basis, although our investigations have successfully led us to France, one must ask if the journey ends here or if we must travel on further south. For now at least, our sculptors and their origins remain a mystery.

[61]   The official inscription commemorating the patron reads 1507.

Scanning in Space and Time

G. W. FRASER[1] and N. KARIM

1. Introduction

In June 2011, in the parish church of St Michael the Archangel, on a notice board usually reserved for prayer groups and flower rotas, there appeared a poster more suited to Hollywood than to the market town of Framlingham in the county of Suffolk. It said: 'Come and meet the Tomb Raiders'. And, on a Wednesday evening in June 2011, the people of Framlingham did exactly that; they came to listen to Phillip Lindley, the Principal Investigator, describe his AHRC/EPSRC-funded Science and Heritage project *Representing Re-Formation: Reconstructing Renaissance Monuments* and explain why the red dot of a laser scanner had been busy for two whole days translating the effigy of Thomas Howard, third duke of Norfolk, his hands clasped in prayer, his beard sharply pointed, lying up there beside his wife, on top of their monumental limestone tomb, into a point cloud of three-dimensional coordinates.

Representing Re-Formation featured a truly inter-disciplinary team. This chapter describes some contributions of space science to the business of Tomb Raiding, concentrating mainly on those unexpected problems and new insights which arose during the three years of the live project and which were not anticipated at its start. The involvement of the University of Leicester Space Research Centre (SRC) in an inter-disciplinary project with its focus in Art History had been expected to be concentrated in two workpackages:

1. in the acquisition of 3D virtual representations of the Howard tombs as they stand now in Framlingham and of the components associated with the monuments, excavated in Thetford; and the manipulation of these virtual objects in an appropriate computer environment to help the art historians puzzle out the original tomb designs as intended to stand in the church of Thetford Priory.
2. in the use of portable X-ray fluorescence (PXRF) to determine the origin of the limestone(s) used in the construction of the tombs. Portable XRF is in widespread use in the Heritage sector and is a very well-documented technique for non-destructive elemental analysis of paints and metal alloys.[2]

---

[1]   This essay was written, but not completed, by Professor George Fraser before his sudden death in March 2014. The editor has completed it, interpolating some commentary (of course without Professor Fraser's having had a chance to discuss it) and excised the incomplete sections. The PhD student Professor Fraser was supervising is Nishad Karim, who amended several of the figures.

[2]   R. Cesareo et al., 'Portable systems for energy-dispersive X-ray fluorescence analysis

Regarding workpackage (1), a review of scanning technologies carried out towards the start of the project indicated that the most cost-effective approach was to hire a commercial company, operating high-capital-value (~£150k) laser scanners, to acquire the tomb images (at a specified surface resolution of 0.1 mm in x and y) in a matter of days, rather than requiring project team members to attempt to scan ~40 square metres of highly-carved limestone with a portable scanner (Picoscanner) of a type affordable (<£10k) to the project.[3] This certainly turned out to be the correct decision; Figure 1 (indicating feature resolution) shows the virtual image of a mason's mark from the third duke's tomb while Figure 2 (indicating surface coverage) shows the first proper view of that tomb's east end, three shell-headed niches each framing a carved figure, rebuilt close against the wall of St. Michael's church, that anyone had had in four-and-a-half centuries. The actual contribution of the SRC in the scanning domain was therefore 'downstream' from the actual scanning, in the investigation of the mechanical properties of the virtual objects and their recreation, in scale model form, using Additive Manufacture –the family name for the various engineering processes more commonly referred to as Rapid Prototyping. This work, described briefly in Section 2, may have some quite general applications in Museum Studies. For the selected contractor, the project offered a successful entry point into the Heritage sector, leading to the establishment of a dedicated subsidiary company.

In the case of workpackage (2), the real expertise of the SRC in both portable XRF and portable XRD (X-ray diffraction), acquired for the Beagle 2 and Exomars Mars missions, was hardly employed at all in the present Science and Heritage context. Assignment of quarries-of-origin to the supposed two distinct limestone phases of the tomb monuments using X-ray trace element analysis is hardly feasible. Studies of Norman Caen stone suggests that its definite identification in medieval buildings and monumental stonework depends on secondary characteristics such as included microfossil types. Section 3 describes instead the use of UV-visible reflectance spectroscopy, an analytical technique to investigate trace polychromy on stone statuary, to test the hypothesis that the tombs of the third Howard duke and of his son-in-law the duke of Richmond, were constructed in two separate phases.

of works of art,' Chapter 9 of Philip J. Potts and Margaret West (eds), *Portable X-ray Fluorescence Spectrometry: Capabilities for in situ Analysis*, Royal Society of Chemistry 2008, 206–46.

3   Europac3D Ltd., Cranham Court, Arden Square, Crewe Business Park, Crewe, Cheshire, CW1 6UA.

2. Interpretation of Laser-Scanned Virtual Objects

The practical usefulness of a computer-based mechanical representation of a satellite instrument or sub-system is in its combination with thermal or vibration analysis packages to simulate the extreme temperatures of the hostile space environment or the vibration loads of launch. Similarly, the scanned Howard tombs stimulated new and unexpected questions for study, once transformed into detailed mass models.

2.1 Mechanical Integrity of the Tombs

The space scientist contemplates the handiwork of the unknown master mason/s of the fifteen-thirties and fifties and asks how much the ducal effigies and their plinth actually weigh, and how is that mass supported? How (if at all) is the thermal expansion of the stone accommodated in the tomb design?

To a first approximation, the mass of each sculpted figure on the third duke's tomb is given by its equivalent cross-sectional area times its length, times the density of a typical limestone, or:

$$\sim[0.25 \times 0.25 \times 2\ ]\ m^3 \times 2300\ kg/m^3 = 287.5\ kg$$

while the plinth itself accounts for another

$$\sim[2 \times 3 \times 0.1 \times 2300] = 1380\ kg.$$

There may be between 1.5–2 metric tonnes of stone resting on the walls of Thomas Howard's tomb.[4]

The thickness of those walls can be immediately and directly estimated from the scanned object itself. The maximum depth of any carved structure must be less than or equal to the minimum wall thickness. Examination of the shell niches which frame the carved prophets and apostles (see Figure 2) then indicates a lower limit to the wall thickness of only ~10 cm. This estimate is confirmed by metrology of tomb fragments unearthed at Thetford including those now held in the British Museum. The third duke and his wife, it seems, may be supported by thin side walls just four inches thick (and by a lion at each corner and by the grace of God), if there are no internal structural supports.

These order-of-magnitude calculations are currently (February 2014) being replaced by precise estimates of the distributions of mass within the complex shapes of the effigies and the forces acting on the tomb walls are being calculated. The internal construction of the tombs may become an important area of future study.

2.2 Mass Distribution of Tomb Component Blocks

While the lids and plinths of the Howard tombs appear monolithic in

---

[4]   Karim estimates, including the four lions, over 3 metric tonnes.

construction, the highly-carved side and end panels are assembled from many individual blocks. The block boundaries have been mapped, in the case of the third duke's tomb, by the archaeological draughtswoman Jill Atherton, working with Phillip Lindley. It is therefore a simple matter to transfer those boundaries to the virtual tomb to establish a mass distribution for the blocks and so gain insights into the handling techniques required in a sixteenth-century mason's yard. In fact, the majority of pieces lie in the mass range 1–20 kg, so that they could have been handled easily by two or three men working together. The transport of the tomb blocks from Thetford to Framlingham would also appear to have been a straightforward exercise for the carters of the day. The blocks of which the main apostle figures were carved, however, were much heavier, and the damage Phillip Lindley has noticed, may be a result of the unanticipated movements of the components, from Thetford to Kenninghall and thence to Framlingham.[5]

2.3 Outgassing of Rapid Prototypes

The 3D additive manufacturing technology (more commonly known as rapid prototyping) used to create solid models of the Howard tombs for the exhibition at Thetford – as they were rebuilt in Framlingham – use plastic or ceramic-like materials to mimic the original limestone. These materials outgas, mostly harmless water vapour, but also more reactive organic compounds such as formaldehyde. As rapid prototyped objects enter the realm of museum display, exhibition organisers need to be sure that those objects are not going to blacken the priceless manuscript placed close beside them in a common display case. Figure 3 shows our measurements of the mass loss from small blocks of one common material used in additive manufacture. The same measurements are also of vital interest to the designers of Cubesats (satellites weighing about one kilogram). In both disciplines, baking the object – model tomb or satellite structure – at modest temperatures for a couple of days removes most of the volatiles trapped in it during manufacture.

3. Optical Reflectance Spectroscopy

A portable optical reflectance spectrometer was used during the June 2011 scanning campaign at Framlingham to attempt to characterise the traces of paint or whitewash that obviously adhere to the Howard tombs. A second set of measurements, made in 2012, may cast light, not on the original colouration of the tombs, but on the differentiation of the stone phases of the monument and the provision of quantitative support for a key art-historical conjecture (fig. 4).

---

[5]   See P. Lindley's essay, above.

4. Conclusions

The Heritage sector is already fully aware of the combined potential of laser scanning and rapid prototyping and is using these technologies to record historical artefacts on all scales, even up to the heroic scale of Stonehenge and Mount Rushmore. The minor contributions of space science, through the medium of the *Representing Re-Formation* project, therefore, have been in demonstrating the potential "added value" of studying the mechanical properties of a scanned object and in cautioning against the indiscriminate use of gas-loaded rapid prototypes. Space science also brings news that additive manufacturing in metal, not plastic, is rapidly advancing in Aerospace. Fragile or corroded metal artefacts can now be recreated in metal. Our project may be the first to have demonstrated this capability. It is certainly in the vanguard of applying optical reflectance spectroscopy to differentiated stone structures.

A sure measure of the success of any interdisciplinary project involving the physical sciences and the humanities is surely evidence that the flow of new ideas has been bi-directional. This is certainly true of *Representing Re-Formation*. Of course, the space scientists, the physicists, know all there is to know about image capture and processing, but the project has highlighted the astonishing progress in portable 3D scanning – from "low cost" to "no cost", in no time at all – and lessons learned from *Representing Re-Formation* will certainly find use in the ongoing programme of planetary science in the Space Research Centre.

But the most important question of all, would we do it again if the opportunity arose?

Of course. Every Tomb Raider adventure has to have a sequel.

Acknowledgements
Nishad Karim gratefully acknowledges the receipt of a project PhD studentship and the support of the Department of Physics and Astronomy. Chris Bicknell provided the optical reflectance measurements and his SRC colleague, Piyal Samara-Ratna, contributed essential expertise in NX and additive manufacture. Thanks also to Jan Summerfield (Senior Curator, English Heritage).

The Surrey Tomb at Framlingham: the Visual Resurrection of a Reputation

LISA FORD

The retrospective tomb-monument to Henry Howard, earl of Surrey, and his wife, Frances de Vere, in the Church of St. Michael in Framlingham (Fig. 1), constructed more than 60 years after Surrey's death in 1547 by their younger son, Henry Howard, earl of Northampton, presents a sharp contrast to the other Howard monuments at Framlingham considered by the *Representing Re-Formation: Reconstructing Renaissance Monuments* project.[1] Unlike the subtle, sophisticated, and stylistically advanced tombs of Thomas Howard, third duke of Norfolk, and Henry Fitzroy, duke of Richmond, with their suggestions of continental influence, Surrey's tomb is an example of what Phillip Lindley describes as a 'traditional monumental type' of the mid-sixteenth to early-seventeenth century: bright polychromy, a profusion of heraldic and status symbols, recumbent effigies, and the figures of the occupants' children.[2] It is not a tomb that suggests either a daring salute to one of the most innovative English poets of the sixteenth century, nor one which attempts to follow the other monuments as a work of groundbreaking artistry in its time. Indeed, as Nigel Llewellyn points out, such an heraldically-dominated tomb would be common-place in a parish church display of the later-sixteenth and early-seventeenth centuries.[3] Rather, the tomb offers a message of stability and a visual restoration of Surrey to his rightful place in the Howard generations and in the chronology of Howard memorialization, as well as visually restoring him to a place of honour, dismissing the nature of his death.[4]

To briefly recap an oft-rehearsed story, Henry Howard, earl of Surrey, was executed on Tower Hill on 19 January 1546/7, convicted of high treason for the display of royal heraldic insignia to which he was allegedly not entitled, and for other actions interpreted as threatening to the secure succession to the throne of Prince Edward, shortly to become Edward VI.[5] Immediately after his execution,

---

[1] The inscription on the tomb makes the date and source clear, stating that 'Henry Howard, Earl of Northampton, their second son, of great piety placed this monument to his parents in the year of our Lord 1614'.

[2] Phillip Lindley, *Tomb Destruction and Scholarship*, Donington 2007, 35.

[3] Nigel Llewellyn, *Funeral Monuments in Post-Reformation England*, Cambridge 2000, 6.

[4] L. Stone & H. M. Colvin, 'The Howard Tombs at Framlingham, Suffolk', *Archaeological Journal*, 122 (1965), 168, remarks 'As the son of the third and the father of the fourth Duke, [Surrey] had an obvious place in the array of family tombs ...'

Surrey's body was laid to rest somewhere in the church or churchyard of All Hallows by the Tower, Barking.[6] At some point between that time and 1614, the body was removed to Framlingham, where it was apparently confirmed to be resting underneath the tomb in 1835.[7] There is little to document either the burial or removal: the extant parish registers of All Hallows recording births, marriages and deaths go back only to 1558, and a list appended to one of the registers of notable burials prior to that time states simply that Surrey was buried at All Hallows 'and removed from there soon after'.[8] This statement was written by the curate who compiled the list in 1860, and there appears to exist no other evidence for the precise time of Surrey's removal.

It does not appear that a tomb for Surrey ever existed at Thetford, or was ever intended for the Framlingham church prior to Northampton's decision in the early seventeenth century to construct one there. In his plea to Henry VIII not to close Thetford Priory in 1540, Thomas Howard, the third duke, mentioned the tombs that were being constructed for himself and Richmond, but did not mention one for Surrey.[9] Surrey was then still quite young, and unlike the third duke and the fourth duke, his wife did not pre-decease him, so there would have been no need to start construction on a memorial for them at that time, and though his wife was buried in St. Michael's, Framlingham after her death in 1577, there is no mention of a tomb or memorial for her.[10] When the family mausoleum was reconstituted at Framlingham, the chancel at St Michael's certainly had been enlarged sufficiently in the mid-sixteenth century to have encompassed a tomb for Surrey as well as those which were erected for the third duke, the duke of Richmond, the fourth duke's two wives, and Elizabeth Howard, the infant daughter of the fourth duke. In their article on the Howard tombs, Lawrence Stone and Howard Colvin speculated that fragments from an unfinished tomb left at Thetford were part of an abandoned tomb for Surrey, but Richard Marks instead argues that they were meant for the two tombs of the third duke and Richmond, for designs that were later abandoned.[11]

[5]   See Peter R. Moore, 'The Heraldic Charge against the Earl of Surrey, 1546–47', *English Historical Review*, 116 (2001), 557–83 for extensive analysis of the heraldic charges.
[6]   *Oxford Dictionary of National Biography*, H. C. G. Matthew and Brian Harrison (eds), Oxford 2004, 361–6; Jessie Childs, *Henry VIII's Last Victim: The Life and Times of Henry Howard, Earl of Surrey*, New York 2007; W. A. Sessions, *Henry Howard, the Poet Earl of Surrey: a Life*, Oxford 1999.
[7]   Gerald Brenan and Edward Phillips Statham, *The House of Howard* (New York 1908), 434.
[8]   London Metropolitan Archives, P69/ALH1/A/01/00.
[9]   The National Archives, SP 1/156, f. 115.
[10] Cokayne, *Complete Peerage*, 9, 621.
[11] Stone & Colvin, 'Howard tombs', 168. Richard Marks, 'The Howard Tombs at

As for the political advisability of creating a tomb for Surrey prior to the early seventeenth century, the intermittent precariousness of the family's existence may have made it either financially impossible, or politically risky, to attempt the restoration of Surrey to his place among the Howard line in such a strongly visual sense. With the third duke imprisoned during Edward VI's reign, and the fourth duke executed during Elizabeth's, and with Northampton spending Elizabeth's reign in a largely uneasy relationship with the queen, the Howard family had little chance for memorial building during the second half of the sixteenth century. Besides Surrey at All Hallows, the bodies of the two Howard queens remained in their graves in the Tower, joined there later in the century by the bodies of the fourth duke and his son, Philip Howard, earl of Arundel. Philip Howard's body was removed from the Tower in 1624, but the others remained in their graves in the chapel.[12]

Other families also appeared disinclined to reclaim the bodies of executed traitors or resurrect them through the building of new and costly or separate monuments. Margaret More Roper is famous for the supposed retrieval of her father's head from London Bridge, but if that tale is true the head of Sir Thomas More appears to have been quietly buried with her, at her request; Margaret Pole, countess of Salisbury was buried in the Tower and never removed to the chantry chapel she had built for herself in Christ Church Priory.[13] Some descendants did attempt more subtle revivals or whitewashing of reputations through existing monuments. Edward Seymour, duke of Somerset, executed in 1552, is lauded in the inscription on his wife Anne's and daughter Jane's tombs in Westminster Abbey as 'the renowned prince Edward duke of Somerset'; the inscription on the Duchess' tomb includes all his titles and accomplishments and no mention of his fate, but no effigy of him was added. John, duke of Northumberland is mentioned on both of his sons' tombs in the Beauchamp Chapel at Warwick, but merely as progenitor. The only other Howard to receive a proper reburial was Philip Howard, earl of Arundel, who died in 1595 while a prisoner in the Tower, and was buried in his father's grave in St. Peter ad Vincula. His remains were removed in 1624 to West Horsley in Surrey by means of special licence granted to his family, and from there removed again to Arundel

Thetford and Framlingham: New Discoveries', *Archaeological Journal* 141 (1984), 261–2. See also Lindley in the present volume.

[12] Doyne C Bell, *Notices of the Historic Persons Buried in the Chapel of St. Peter ad Vincula, in the Tower of London. With an Account of the Discovery of the Supposed Remains of Queen Anne Boleyn*, London 1877, 19–31 for discussion of examination of remains in St. Peter ad Vincula and reinterrment of some during restoration in 1876–7.

[13] H. O. Albin, 'Opening of the Roper Vault in St. Dunstan's Canterbury and Thoughts on the Burial of William and Margaret Roper', *Moreana* 63 (1979), 29–35.

and quietly interred in the family vault. On 10 March 1971, his remains were again removed to Arundel Cathedral following his canonisation in 1970.[14]

Even royalty might hesitate to memorialize treasonous ancestors. Elizabeth I, though she acknowledged her mother through the occasional use of Anne Boleyn's falcon badge, and the wearing of a ring with Anne's portrait, made no attempt to rehabilitate her mother's reputation through memorialization or removal of her body to a more fitting resting place.[15] The bones believed to be those of Anne Boleyn remain in St. Peter ad Vincula, reinterred in the 1870s after being exhumed during renovations to the chapel, and throughout her life Elizabeth tended to identify herself most closely with her paternal rather than maternal inheritance.[16] James VI wrote letters to Elizabeth I prior to his mother's execution, requesting mercy for Mary, and protesting the damage that such an execution would do to Elizabeth's reputation and to the sacral nature of kingship.[17] However, upon Mary's death, he retreated into acquiescence, apparently fearful of alienating Elizabeth and her ministers and being cut off as heir to the English throne. The grand tomb which he finally built for his mother in Westminster Abbey, and to which he removed Mary Stuart's body, developed only after he had become king, and after plans had been devised for a monument for Queen Elizabeth.[18]

Peter Sherlock has traced the plans for Mary Stuart's tomb, showing that the construction of a tomb for the Scottish Queen was prompted by the persistent efforts of Elizabeth's former minister, Robert Cecil, to create a seemly monument for the recently deceased English queen, and that, as those plans took form, James moved to ensure the creation of an even grander monument than that of Elizabeth for his mother.[19] Not only was Mary Stuart's tomb larger and more expensive than Elizabeth's, but the iconography presents her as both a divinely ordained ruler, and one with an impressive royal heritage, linked most immediately to that of Henry VII, the founder of the Tudor line.[20] The manner of her death was made explicit, but in a way that framed it as a lesson to others

---

[14] Arundel Castle Archives, Miscellaneous Documents 1688, memorandum by F. W. Steer on transfer of remains from Fitzalan Chapel to Arundel Cathedral 10 March 1971, by kind permission of His Grace the Duke of Norfolk.

[15] Christopher Haigh, *Elizabeth I*, London and New York 1988, 3.

[16] Bell, *Notices of the Historic Persons Buried in the Chapel of St. Peter ad Vincula*, 20–21.

[17] G. P. V. Akrigg, *Letters of King James VI & I*, Berkeley, 1984, 74–85, passim.

[18] Peter Sherlock, 'The Monuments of Elizabeth Tudor and Mary Stuart: King James and the Manipulation of Memory', *The Journal of British Studies* 46/2 (2007), 269–70. This essay is the most authoritative discussion of these two tombs.

[19] Sherlock, *Monuments*, 273–80.

[20] Sherlock, *Monuments*, 280.

not to collude in the death of monarchs.[21] Ultimately, the tomb presents Mary Stuart as a noble martyr whose transmission of the right to the English throne to her son redeems her.

Did this royal project inspire Northampton to pursue the same visual redemption for his father? Sherlock suggests that Northampton 'followed the king's lead in remedying the tragedies of his own family history' when he caused the Surrey monument to be built, and certainly James' actions may have prompted Northampton to speculate that such a project would be viewed sympathetically, perhaps even more so considering Northampton's own involvement in the memorialization of the Stuart Queen.[22] Northampton was not only among the councilors involved in the construction of Mary Stuart's tomb, but he also wrote text for the epitaph and elegiac verses which appear upon the monument, and his admiration of Mary roused Elizabeth's suspicions of his loyalties during Mary's lifetime sufficiently to warrant his imprisonment.[23] Northampton also enjoyed a close and generally warm relationship with James, who credited him with being among those who faithfully and diligently promoted James' claim to the throne during Elizabeth's reign.[24]

Northampton's own strong feelings about what was due to his family name and honour no doubt played a major part in this visual rehabilitation of his father. That Northampton felt deeply, and with bitterness and rancour, the fall of his family, and the shame of the penury and isolation that he endured in his years in the political wilderness is clear in his correspondence. In an undated letter to Elizabeth, after informing the Queen that he had been told "your Maiestye desired no mannes head in England halfe so much as myne," he commented, "If my life will satisfie your indignatione I resigne it willingelye, as one I vowe before almighty God that wold more gladlie shorten and abbridge my wretchid daies without offence to god, then liue beneath the compas of my birth and euer pine in wante as I haue bene constrayned to doo, rather then I wold estrannge my selfe from the presence ore the seruice of your Maiesty."[25] In letters of 1571 and 1572 to William Cecil, Lord Burleigh, to whom he appealed for intervention when he encountered financial difficulties or when he felt his life and liberty were under threat during Elizabeth's reign, he speaks of Cecil's kindness

[21] Sherlock, *Monuments*, 279–80.
[22] Sherlock, *Monuments*, 288.
[23] Sherlock, *Monuments*, 277–81 analyses the epitaph in great detail.
[24] James expresses such sentiments in a letter of c. 1602 to Howard, in *The Secret Correspondence of Sir Robert Cecil with James VI King of Scotland*, Edinburgh and London 1766, 119; see also L. L. Peck, *Northampton: Patronage and Policy at the Court of James I*, London 1992, 23 for comments on James' reception of Henry Howard on his arrival in England and their first meeting, and her assessment of their relationship throughout the reign.
[25] BL Titus C VI. ff 5v–6r. Undated letter of Henry Howard to Queen Elizabeth I.

'toward the poore remayne of our unhappy howse,' and turns to him during the period of the fourth duke's trial for help, indicating that with his brother's fall, he had no one to assist him with finances, nothing settled on him, and not even a certain place to live, as friends were afraid to offer assistance lest they provoke the Queen's displeasure.[26]

From such depths of misery and isolation, Northampton rose to the height of his personal power in James' reign, and by the end of his life he was wealthy, titled, and secure in the king's favour, and apparently determined to re-establish the fame of his house. In his father's tomb one can see the re-establishment of a positive reputation for Surrey and a proper memorial for him and his wife. As Nigel Llewellyn has discussed, the recumbent armoured figure evokes both ideas of ancient lineage and of knightly valour, identifying those virtues with the person represented.[27] The inscription on the tomb indicates only that he suffered an 'untimely' death with no hint of its nature.[28] Garbed in armour, peerage robes and garter insignia, Surrey reclaims his good name.

The tomb may also serve as the stealthy fulfillment of the fourth duke's memorial wishes and the restoration of the final link in the memorial chain represented by the Framlingham tombs. The will of Thomas Howard, fourth duke of Norfolk, requested that his body be buried in St. Michael's in Framlingham, 'there layde in that Tombe, where my lovinge Wyves are buryed; Willinge my Executors to bestowe no further Charge of any newe Tombe upon me, otherwyse then a Statue of me either sett in the wall, or layd upon that Tombe, as theye shall thynke moste ffyttest'.[29] The space between the two wives' effigies where that 'Statue' would have gone remains empty, nor is there an image in the walls next to the tomb, but a representation of the fourth duke does exist near to his intended resting space. His kneeling image on the Surrey monument (Fig. 2), clad in his peerage robes and garter collar, is at the feet of his parents' effigies, along with that of his similarly clad brother, Northampton, and facing the tomb of his two wives, with no other monument or object intervening. It is tempting to consider whether Northampton chose this style of monument, with its kneeling figures, partly as a subtle means of providing a reinstatement of his brother to the family representations.

However, the style of tomb also suggests the placing of Surrey in his proper place in the Howard generations, and his own frame of reference among the

---

[26] BL Titus C VI. ff. 13v, 17r.

[27] Nigel Llewellyn, 'Honour in Life, Death and in the Memory: Funeral Monuments in Early Modern England', *Transactions of the Royal HIstorical Society* 6 (1996), 197–8.

[28] The inscription reads 'immature anno salutis mdxlvi abrepto'.

[29] Arundel Castle Archives, Testamentary Records, T5, Copy of the will of Thomas, fourth Duke of Norfolk, by kind permission of His Grace the Duke of Norfolk.

peerage. As mentioned above, Surrey's tomb differs stylistically from the other tombs at Framlingham, and is of a later style than the brasses inlaid into 'marble' slabs that were raised to his relatives at Lambeth in the early- to mid-sixteenth century. It also differs from the classicized tomb of his son, Northampton (Fig. 3), which was commissioned and executed at roughly the same time, but whose style was in keeping with that coming into fashion among Northampton's peers in the early seventeenth century.[30] In point of fact, Surrey's tomb most closely resembles the tombs of Ambrose Dudley, earl of Warwick (d. 1590) (Fig. 4) and Robert Dudley, earl of Leicester (d. 1588), at St. Mary's, Warwick, those of Francis Russell, second earl of Bedford (d. 1585) and Anne Russell, countess of Warwick (d. 1604) at Chenies, and that of William Bourchier, earl of Bath (d. 1623), at Tawstock, Devon (d. 1623) (Fig. 5), thus embodying a style that can be seen among the tombs of the peerage through the Elizabethan/Jacobean period. Despite their troubled lives, the Howards were a sturdy and long-lived race; John Howard, first duke of Norfolk, was probably about 60 years old when he died fighting on the field at Bosworth; Thomas Howard, the second duke was probably 80 at his death, and Thomas Howard, the third duke was 80 or 81. Had Surrey lived a span comparable to his forebears, he might well have been buried in a similar time period to the Dudleys and Bedfords, and in just such a tomb.

Northampton's rationale must remain conjectural, as there appears to be no information regarding his motivations. His will directs his executors to bury him and to build his own tomb 'in the Auncient Chappell within the Castle of Dover', but says nothing in reference to his parents' tomb.[31] The inscription on the Surrey tomb itself dates it to 1614, the year of Northampton's death, but whether it was completed prior to his death or not is unclear. The inscription stone credits Northampton with placing the tomb there to honour his parents (Fig. 6), but the task of completing the tomb and securing its future may well have been borne entirely by Northampton's secretary and chief administrator of his will, John Griffith. Both Northampton's tomb and Surrey's feature inscription stones heralding John Griffith's oversight of their completion (Figs 7 and 8).[32]

---

[30] Lisa L. Ford, 'A Body in Motion: The Afterlives of the Tomb of Henry Howard, Earl of Northampton', *Material Culture Review* 74–5 (2013) / *Revue de la culture matérielle* 74–5 (Spring 2013), 161–73.

[31] E. P. Shirley (ed.), 'An Inventory of the Effects of Henry Howard, K.G., Earl of Northampton, taken on his Death in 1614, together with a Transcript of his Will', *Archaeologia* 42 (1869), 375.

[32] On Northampton's tomb, an inscription stone reads "Iohanne Griffitho huic Comiti ab epistolis curante Positum" [Erected by the care of John Griffith secretary to this Earl]; the inscription on the Surrey tomb reads "Iohanne Griffitho Nuper Comiti Northamptoniae ab epistolis curante" [By the care of John Griffith secretary to the

Griffith's papers provide no further enlightenment regarding the contract and construction of the Surrey tomb, nor do they identify its sculptor, though they do offer glimpses of its completion such as the putting in place of grates around Surrey's and Northampton's tombs, and the setting in place of annuities to pay keepers for each tomb. Griffith was kept fully occupied on the business of settling Northampton's bequests and foundations for at least ten years after the earl's death, and among his notes are several examples which mark the progress of the tombs and the work necessary to provide for their future maintenance. In Griffith's accounts and memoranda relating to Northampton's estate business, a document dated 27 September, 1616 bears the notation 'A note aswell of the mony to be receaved as also of the Debtes and Legacyes to be paid, the workes and other thinges yet to be performed' from Northampton's estate, and on the list is 'Item for my Lo: Tombe and the Earle of Surreys the grates and the Annutyes to be bought for keeping of them ...', which was to cost £440.[33] The first payment to the keeper assigned to care for the Surrey tomb may have been made as early as 1616, and working through the various receipts after that, one sees scattered notations of the payments.[34] On 9 November, 1623, there is note of the disbursements to the sexton at Framlingham church 'for lookinge to the Earle of Surrey his tombe'; similar payments were being made to someone at Dover who had been chosen as the keeper of Northampton's own tomb.[35] In addition, the keepers at both Dover and Framlingham were reimbursed for any repairs or additions required; again in 1623, regarding the Surrey tomb, a note was made, though no figure was appended, of money paid to 'mr fuller a servant of my Lo: of Suffolke, beinge money by him disbursed for reparacons done about yt isle in ye church Where ye tombe standith ... & a lock for the Grate about ye tomb.' That Griffith was winding up his tenure as the facilitator of these payments in that same year is suggested by his note below these sums, 'Item that these Annuityes are hereafter as they be receyved to be payd to the Warden of the hospitall at Grenwich & he is accordinge to statute to pay them severally in one entyre payment yearlie at Allhallowtyde, in such sorte as therin is provided for ye mayntenance of ye sayd tombes'.[36] An indenture dated 1625 lays out in precise detail the basis for the funding and mechanism of the yearly payments to the tomb keepers.[37]

late Earl of Northampton].

[33]   National Library of Wales (NLW) Carreglwyd Papers, 372, Series I, f. 1r.
[34]   Mercers' Company Archives (MCA), Miscellaneous MS 9.7.
[35]   NLW Carreglwyd Papers, 398, Series I.
[36]   Ibid.
[37]   MCA, Charles Tatham Curious Ancient Documents, part of uncatalogued documents, Trinity Hospital #14.

Subsequent receipts at the Mercers' Company show that system in action. A receipt of 28 November 1626, states that the churchwardens of the parish church of Framlingham received 26s. 8d. on that date from Abraham Nottingham, Warden of Trinity Hospital in East Greenwich, 'for one whole years Annuity due at the feast of All Saints last past towards the maintenance of the Isle of the said Churche were the tombe of the Earle & Countesse of Surrey standeth', as well as 13s. 4d. 'for one whole years Annuity due at the feast of All Saintes last past for keepinge the tombe erected in the said church for the Earle and Countesse of Surrey'.[38] Similar receipts can be found in the Mercers' accounts through at least 1754, and even now St. Michael's church receives funds yearly from the Mercers' Company to assist with the upkeep of the tomb.[39]

Surrey's tomb has the ironic distinction of being one of the most securely settled and least changed of the Howard tombs over the past five centuries. The movement of two of the other Howard tombs between Thetford and Framlingham has been a main focus of *Representing Re-Formation*. The Howard tombs at Lambeth, including a second tomb erected to Thomas Howard, the great second duke, to replace the one at Thetford, have disappeared, and are only preserved through their images in an illuminated early-seventeenth-century genealogy. Northampton's own tomb has a volatile history, having been removed from Dover to the earl's foundation of Trinity Hospital in Greenwich, when the chapel in Dover Castle where it rested began crumbling in the late seventeenth century due to neglect, and was deemed a danger to the tomb.[40] But Surrey's tomb appears never to have moved, though in the 1970s weakness in the foundation and subsidence of the tomb after four centuries necessitated a major programme of repair. The Surrey tomb sits in what appears to have been its original spot, in the north aisle; as stated earlier, early receipts for payment to keepers of the tomb at Framlingham mention the 'Isle of the said Churche were the tombe of the Earle & Countesse of Surrey standeth'.[41] And unless it was drastically altered from its original design, the tomb structure itself, with a truncated upper portion of the platform for the effigies on the side nearest the church wall, suggests that it was meant to sit close against that wall, rather than be accessible from all four sides.

During its restoration in 1976, the tomb was completely dismantled, and stripped of many of the layers of paint that had been applied over the centuries

---

[38] MCA, Trinity Hospital 1/125/22.

[39] MCA, Charles Tatham Curious Ancient Documents, part of uncatalogued documents, Trinity Hospital, #114 for 1754 receipt. I am indebted to Jane Ruddell, Archivist, Curator and Records Manager, for the information regarding the current annual contribution.

[40] See Ford, 'A Body in Motion', for the full history of the tomb.

[41] MCA, Trinity Hospital 1/125/22, receipt dated 28 November 1626.

to the heraldic decorations and the inscription panels, and the effigies were cleaned and their robes retouched. The report of the work done to the tomb by one John A. Green details many interesting points, including that Surrey's effigy 'had been broken before it had been fixed when the tomb was being first erected' and Green traces the steps taken by the early workmen to secure the pieces together on top of the tomb.[42] The twentieth-century workmen apparently did not penetrate to the area below the tomb: no mention is made of finding bones or remains, and photos taken during the restoration suggest that they cleared just to ground level, to lay a new foundation for the tomb which would properly support the structure (Fig. 9). They also consulted with Sir Anthony Wagner, Garter King of Arms, regarding the coats of arms, to ensure that their recolouring was accurate. Missing pieces, such as balls on the alabaster coronets, were replaced, and the ermine retouched on the effigies' robes. But the final memorial to the volatile earl, a man who was once arrested for vandalism committed during a carouse through the London streets, seems to have enjoyed the most stable afterlife of his family's memorials.

Among the most curious elements of the Surrey tomb is the perambulating coronet that currently rests just below the effigy's right knee (Fig. 10). Green's report mentions regilding the coats of arms, the garter collars on the earl and his sons, the edges of the earl's armour, and the heraldic beasts, but it describes only regilding 'the coronets on the earl's wife and daughter, also the headbands on the two younger daughters', with no mention made of any coronet for the earl. What is certain is that during the life of the tomb, the coronet has shifted places, been replaced at least once, and has been altogether absent at other times. A watercolour dated c. 1907, does not show a coronet near the knee, and it is not possible to determine if one is visible on the cushion near the effigy's head, while an image from a publication of the same period, said to show the tomb in the 1890s, does show the coronet by the knee,[43] and seems likely to be after engravings of the tomb from 1748 and 1797 (Fig. 11). But in a *Country Life* article from June 1929 the coronet is described as lying 'on the cushions in close proximity to his head'.[44] This assertion cannot be verified from the photographs accompanying that article, but a publication of 1923 indeed shows a coronet, of a different style to the current one, in that position (Fig. 12). The placement

[42] The Church of St. Michael, Framlingham, Archives. Letter dated 6 December 1976, from John A. Green.

[43] Images at http://www.british-towns.net/england/eastern/suffolk/suffolk-coastal/ framlingham/album/tomb-of-henry-howard and at http://www.british-towns.net/ england/eastern/suffolk/suffolk-coastal/framlingham/album/henry-howard-earl-of- surrey

[44] Lady Victoria Manners, 'The Howard Tombs at Framlingham', *Country Life* (June 29, 1929), 950.

seems to correspond to small holes that can still be seen on the cushion that supports the earl's head (Fig. 13), and the coronet appears still to have been in that position when restoration of the tomb began in 1976 (Fig 14). In photos taken around the time of the repair and restoration of the tomb, some show a coronet, and some do not (Fig. 15). Due to its fragile and damaged state it was removed and a new one made, which would also explain why Surrey's coronet was not mentioned among the regilded elements. The old coronet was thought to have been lost, but was rediscovered during this research, and does look like the one that is shown on the cushion near the earl's head in the 1923 publication (Fig. 16).[45] However, when the new coronet was placed on the tomb, it was placed by Surrey's knee, as seen in photos from newspaper accounts on the day the tomb was reconsecrated, 9 July, 1977, in a grand service attended by members of the Howard family, led by the seventeenth duke of Norfolk (Fig. 17). Besides its absence immediately after the restoration, as a new one was created, a possible explanation for the absence of the coronet in earlier images, as put forth in discussion with one of the St. Michael churchwardens, Sandra Cartwright, is that such a fragile bit of sculpture suffered damage or loss over the centuries and was replaced, perhaps more than once.

The coronet is mentioned in several publications as resting near Surrey's knee as a sign of the earl being executed and degraded from his title, which would bear an interesting comparison to the fact that the effigy of Mary Stuart is not wearing a crown or coronet, but simply a cap.[46] That interpretation may bear further examination, as it does not appear to be based on heraldic stricture, nor does it correspond with the circumstances of other, much later, tombs on which the coronet rests near the figure, such as that of Thomas Coventry, 1st earl of Coventry at St. Mary, Elmley Castle (d. 1699) (Fig. 18). There, the coronet is meant as a commentary on setting aside earthly glory, not a marker of shame, though Coventry's tomb itself provoked controversy due to fabrications in the heraldry and inscription relating to his wife's lineage.[47] But a coronet appearing

[45] I am indebted to Sandra Cartwright, St. Michael's churchwarden, and the Reverend Canon David Pitcher, Rector at the time of the restoration, for this information. St. Michael's still possesses the discarded coronet, which, as Rev. Pitcher attested at its removal 'was missing many details and had little colouring or gold leaf."

[46] For example, Cox, *English Church Fittings*, 60, states 'as he was beheaded in 1547, his coronet lies by his side'.

[47] For an excellent discussion of the Elmley monument and others which display this iconography, see Brian Kemp, *English Church Monuments*, London 1980, 168–9. I am indebted to members of the Church Monuments Society for directing me to the image in Cox's book of the Surrey tomb with the coronet on the pillow, and to the Elmley Castle tomb, and for discussion regarding the possible meaning of the placement of the coronet. For the lineage issue, see John G. Nichols (ed.), *The Herald and Genealogist* 7, London 1873, 100–10.

on the effigial tomb of an executed traitor may be unique to Surrey. There is the additional puzzle of the early seventeenth-century watercolour with gold illumination of the tomb, which does not show a coronet next to the knee of Surrey, but does show one by the right knee of the figure of his eldest son, Thomas, fourth duke of Norfolk, who was also executed for treason (Fig. 19). No such object now exists in that place on the tomb. Was the coronet and that implication orginally attached to the fourth duke, or is this an error on the part of the artist?

A further argument might be made that it rested either next to Surrey's head or near his knee because he was earl of Surrey by courtesy only, not by proper title; he is frequently referred to as 'styled Earl of Surrey' in modern reference sources.[48] If Surrey's coronet is meant to indicate his disgrace and degredation from rank one might expect the same would apply to the insignia of the Order of the Garter, prominent on the tomb and effigy. Surrey was degraded upon his attainder, so presumably he would no longer be entitled to display such insignia. However, in the iconography of the tomb, Surrey is restored to his pre-death honours; indeed a note from Samuel Thompson, Windsor Herald, which appears to be instructions for the tomb sculptor says 'you muste make my Lord as he goeth to the parlament in his Robes' and to depict Surrey's 'Armes wth helme Creaste and supporters' so it would appear the depiction of him in garter insignia and peerage robes was not seen as subversive.[49]

Perhaps Surrey's memorialization with these honours was acceptable due to his growing reputation as one of England's greatest poets, a talent worthy of comparison with any European poet, combined with suggestions that his life was sacrificed on admittedly thin grounds. Only ten years after his death, volumes of verse by Surrey and Sir Thomas Wyatt, another victim of Henry VIII's persecutions, were being published with a preface explaining that the publisher sought to share the riches of English verse by these two men, worthy to be compared with great Italian and Latin poets, 'to the honour of the Englishe

---

[48]   E. B. Fryde et al. (eds), *Handbook of British Chronology*, 3rd edn, repr. with corrections, Cambridge & New York 1996, 485; Peter J. Begent and Hubert Chesshyre, *The Most Noble Order of the Garter: 650 years*, London 1999, 315; http://www.royalcollection.org.uk/microsites/knightsofthegarter/MicroObject.asp? row=3&themeid=459&item=4. His current DNB biography also states 'he was never a peer'. Susan Brigden, 'Howard, Henry, Earl of Surrey (1516/17–1547)', *Oxford Dictionary of National Biography*, Oxford University Press, 2004; online edn, Jan 2008 [http://www.oxforddnb.com/view/article/13905, accessed 27 March 2013].

[49]   Arundel Castle Archives, Genealogical/Family papers 1/8, by kind permission of His Grace the Duke of Norfolk. The same might also be argued of the figure of Thomas Howard, fourth duke of Norfolk, who also wears his peerage robes and garter insignia on the figure on his father's tomb.

tongue and for profite of the studious of Englishe eloquence ...'.[50] The only apparent reference to Surrey's fate is contained in the printer's comment that he hopes his reader will not think it 'evill done' to publish these works.[51] William Sessions' literary biography of Surrey mentions also his *Aeneid*, published in September 1554, as a first translation of that text into blank verse, invented by Surrey, thus achieving a moment of high significance and renown for the poetic works of an English nobleman.[52] With the printing of his poetry from 1557, his reputation as England's noble poet grew, as did recognition of the flimsiness of his attainder. Sessions comments that through the early Marian recognition of his poetry, and through the poet Thomas Chaloner's representation of him as falsely accused and brought down by envy, Surrey rapidly attained the status of martyr rather than traitor.[53]

The iconography of the tomb, however, makes no attempt to invoke the reputation that Surrey had acquired by the time of its creation, as one of the most renowned English poets of the sixteenth century. Though himself a poetic innovator, ironically Surrey is represented to the world in a conservative fashion; as a nobleman of rank and importance, father of a resplendent family, themselves laden with honours, in a tomb heavily decorated with heraldic insignia, and no traces of religious imagery or texts. The addition of a tomb for Surrey and his wife to the monuments at Framlingham thus accomplishes much the same purpose as the countless Tudor-Jacobean pattern portraits that filled long galleries, some also done posthumously. Northampton himself had 'Eight pictures of the howse of Norfolk from John duke of Norfolk to the Lord Matravers now beinge', in a gallery at Northampton House in London.[54] Like those portraits, the Surrey tomb fills a gap in the monumental genealogy of a great house, restoring to Surrey his honours, titles, and rightful place among his family.

---

[50]   *Songes and Sonnettes, written by the Right Honorable Lord Henry Haward, Late Earle of Surrey, and Other* (Richard Tottel, 1557).
[51]   ibid.
[52]   Sessions, *Surrey*, 268.
[53]   Sessions, *Surrey*, 271, 291.
[54]   Shirley, 'An inventory of the Effects of Henry Howard, K.G.', *Archaeologia* 42 (1869), 356.

PICTURE CAPTIONS AND CREDITS

Jackie Hall

1. Aerial view of the priory, looking north (© English Heritage).
2. Prior's Lodging, looking north-east; note re-used Romanesque arches in centre of building. The building stands west of the church, facing the gatehouse to the north (Tom Arber).
3. Eastern arm of church, showing known and probable tomb and screen locations (Jackie Hall using English Heritage plan).
4. Fragment of painted and gilded cornice from a late medieval screen, 11.6cm wide (Jackie Hall).
5. Tympanum, with lion (c.35cm wide) – one of many fine Romanesque sculptured and architectural pieces surviving from the early priory (© Norwich Castle Museum and Art Gallery).
6. The church, looking east, with the nave altar in the foreground and the high altar, raised on steps, in the middle distance (Tom Arber).
7. Horse harness, c.3cm wide (Jackie Hall).
8. Pilgrim badge (c.4.7cm high), late 15th-century, with an annunciation scene (Jackie Hall).
9. Fragment of delicate Perpendicular screenwork, c.13.5cm high (Jackie Hall).
10. Hollow spiral shaft (outer diameter, c.5.8cm), part of an ornate and original composition, perhaps around or on top of a tomb (Jackie Hall).
11. Bunch of grapes (c.5cm high) from top of a hollow spiral shaft carved as a vine (Jackie Hall).
12. Fragment of painted wall plaster (c.6cm wide), indicative of the brightly coloured interior that once existed (Jackie Hall).
13. Fragment of plaster cornice (c.22.5cm wide), just possibly from a tomb or tomb canopy. Smaller matching fragments retained gilding on their surface. (Jackie Hall).
14. Map showing the location of the medieval religious houses of Thetford (© Sue White).
15. Late 17th-century view of the priory ruins, looking south-east, by Wenceslas Hollar (© The Pepys Library, Magdalene College, Cambridge).
16. Late-eighteenth-century print of the priory ruins, looking north-west (NMAS: Ancient House, Thetford).
17. Postcard of the priory ruins, c.1910, looking north-east (NMAS: Ancient House, Thetford).
18. Rare photograph of the early clearance excavations, looking east from the crossing, taken on 17th September 1934 (NMAS: Ancient House, Thetford).

Phillip Lindley

1. Tomb monument of Thomas, the third Howard Duke of Norfolk (d. 1554), and his first wife, Anne (d. 1511), daughter of Edward IV, from the south west (Paul Bryan, English Heritage).
2. Tomb monument of Thomas, the third Howard Duke of Norfolk (d. 1554), and his first wife, Anne (d. 1511), daughter of Edward IV, south side (Phillip Lindley).
3. Tomb monument of Thomas, the third Howard Duke of Norfolk (d. 1554), and his first wife, Anne (d. 1511), daughter of Edward IV, north side (Phillip Lindley).
4. Tomb monument of Henry Fitzroy, Duke of Richmond & Somerset (d. 1536) and his wife Duchess Mary [Howard] (d. 1555), from the north west (Paul Bryan, English Heritage).
5. Tomb monument of Henry Fitzroy, Duke of Richmond & Somerset (d. 1536) and his wife Duchess Mary [Howard] (d. 1555) from the south west (Phillip Lindley).
6. Tomb monument of Henry Fitzroy, Duke of Richmond & Somerset (d. 1536) and his wife Duchess Mary [Howard] (d. 1555), south side (Phillip Lindley).
7. Tomb monument of Duchesses Mary Fitzalan (d. 25 August 1557) and Margaret Audley (d. 10 January 1564), the first two of the three wives of Thomas Howard, the fourth duke (d. 1572), from the south west (Phillip Lindley).
8. Tomb monument of the fourth duke's daughter, Elizabeth Howard (d.c. 1565), from the south (Phillip Lindley).
9. Wingless figure holding coat of arms and instruments of Christ's Passion, from Richmond's monument (Phillip Lindley).
10. Carved ducal coronet above coat of arms, Richmond's monument (Phillip Lindley).
11. Old Testament prophet with scroll, on baluster shaft, third duke's monument (Phillip Lindley).
12. Retrospective brass of Catherine Howard, Stoke-by-Nayland, Suffolk (Phillip Lindley).

13. Tomb monument of Thomas Howard, second Duke of Norfolk, depicted by Sir Thomas Wriothesley) , Garter King of Arms, British Library, Additional MS 45131, f. 85 (Copyright The British Library Board).
14. Motte, Thetford Castle (Phillip Lindley)
15. Framlingham Castle (Phillip Lindley).
16. East end of chancel, St Michael's, Framlingham, Suffolk (Phillip Lindley).
17. South aisle of chancel, St Michael's, Framlingham, Suffolk (Phillip Lindley).
18. TNA, LR2/115 (the 1551 version of the inventory), folio 64r (Kate Adcock).
19. Mason's marks, on Richmond monument, also found on third duke's monument (Phillip Lindley).
20. 1555 graffito on Richmond's monument (Phillip Lindley).
21. Detail of the effigy of the third duke (Phillip Lindley).
22. Detail of the effigy of the duchess (Phillip Lindley).
23. Three components of a detached shaft, excavated on the site of Thetford Priory in the 1930s (Phillip Lindley).
24. Three components (of 4) of a half-shaft, excavated on the site of Thetford Priory in the 1930s (Phillip Lindley).
25. Kneeling angel with arms of Christ's Passion (3 nails) excavated on the site of Thetford Priory in the 1930s (Phillip Lindley).
26. Kneeling angel with arms of Christ's Passion (crown of thorns) excavated on the site of Thetford Priory in the 1930s (Phillip Lindley).
27. Angel with the three Magi relief, excavated on the site of Thetford Priory in the 1930s (Phillip Lindley).
28. Fragment of sabaton excavated on the site of Thetford Priory in the 1930s (Phillip Lindley).
29. G. H. Chettle's 1936 hypothesized reconstruction of the monument incorporating the excavated fragments.
30. G. H. Chettle, hypothesized reconstruction of whole monument incorporating the excavated fragments.
31. Old Testament prophet bust-length relief, excavated on the site of Thetford Priory in the nineteenth century (Phillip Lindley).
32. Old Testament king bust-length relief, excavated on the site of Thetford Priory in the nineteenth century (Phillip Lindley).
33. Fragment of Old Testament figure, excavated on the site of Thetford Priory in the 1930s (Phillip Lindley).
34. Detail of Drunkeness of Noah relief, from Richmond's monument, showing flint inclusion (Phillip Lindley).
35. Triangular-shaped repair to Apostle relief from third duke's monument (Phillip Lindley).
36. Detail of St John the Evangelist figure, from the east end of the third duke's monument (Phillip Lindley).
37. Europac laser scanning monuments of fourth duke and Elizabeth Howard, Framlingham (Phillip Lindley).
38. Nishad Karim's virtual disassembly of south side of third duke's monument, based on 3D scans and Lindley and Atherton's identification of individual stones of the monument. Effigies omitted.
39. Nishad Karim's virtual disassembly of east end of third duke's monument, based on 3D scans and Lindley and Atherton's identification of individual stones of the monument. Effigies omitted.
40. Europac scanning British Museum panel (Phillip Lindley).
41. Painted figure wrongly assigned to the components of the third duke's and Richmond's monuments, showing that it is too large to fit where Chettle had placed it in his reconstruction.
42. Figure on baluster shaft, third duke's monument (Phillip Lindley).
43. Head of a figure intended to fit on baluster shaft, third duke's monument, excavated at Thetford Priory in the twentieth century (Phillip Lindley).

44. Comparison of head with those of figures on baluster shaft here identified as part of Richmond's monument, excavated at Thetford Priory in the twentieth century (Phillip Lindley).
45. Disassembly of the monuments showing phasing of components (Ian Drake and Nishad Karim following Lindley and Atherton).
46. Incised numbering marks on top surface of British Museum Old Testament relief panel.
47. Incised number on top surface of Three Magi and angel panel [Fig. 27] (Phillip Lindley).
48. Nishad Karim's conjectural reconstruction of one bay of the third duke's monument as originally planned, with Magi relief incorporated to scale.
49. Nishad Karim's conjectural reconstruction of one bay of Richmond's monument as originally planned, with BM panel, half shaft and base elements incorporated, to scale.
50. Creation of Eve, Richmond's monument, Framlingham (Phillip Lindley).

Rebecca Constabel

1. Framlingham, third Howard duke of Norfolk's tomb (Rebecca Constabel).
2. Tomb of François II and Marguerite de Foix, Nantes (Rebecca Constabel).
3. Tomb of the dukes of Orleans, St Denis (Rebecca Constabel).
4. Tomb of Artus Gouffier, Oiron (Rebecca Constabel).
5. Tomb of Imbert de Batarnay, Montrésor (Rebecca Constabel).
6. Map of Norfolk's route.
7. 1559 date inscribed on the Howard tomb (Phillip Lindley).
8. 1555 date inscribed on Richmond's Tomb (Rebecca Constabel).
9. Graffito on Howard Tomb, south side (Phillip Lindley).
10. Tomb of Raoul de Lannoy (d. 1508) and Jehanne de Poix, Folleville (Rebecca Constabel).
11. Detail, showing Antonio della Porta inscription below the feet of the effigy (Rebecca Constabel).
12. Detail of inscription on the tomb of Artus Gouffier (Rebecca Constabel).
13. Bishop Thomas James's tomb, Dol-de-Bretagne: detail of Gothic inscription (Rebecca Constabel).
14. Bishop Thomas James's tomb, Dol-de-Bretagne (Rebecca Constabel).

G. W. Fraser and N. Karim

1. Mason's individual mark, at centre of image, illustrating sub-mm resolution of laser-scanned virtual tomb.
2. Laser-scanned image of the east end or 'hidden face' of the third Duke's tomb. The height of the tomb to the level of the top plinth is approximately 1.6m. The effigies of the Duke and his wife are not shown.
3. Measurements of the mass loss from small blocks of one common material used in additive manufacture.
4. Optical reflectance spectroscopy results.

Lisa Ford

1. Tomb of Henry Howard, Earl of Surrey, and his wife, Frances de Vere. The Church of St. Michael, Framlingham, Suffolk (Lisa Ford).
2. Figures of Thomas Howard, fourth Duke of Norfolk, left, and Henry Howard, Earl of Northampton, right, from the tomb of Henry Howard, Earl of Surrey. The Church of St. Michael, Framlingham, Suffolk (Lisa Ford).
3. Tomb of Henry Howard, Earl of Northampton, c. 1638, from Henry Lilly MS, G 1/16, f. 130 Arundel Castle Archives. By kind permission of His Grace the Duke of Norfolk
4. Tomb of Ambrose Dudley, Earl of Warwick. Beauchamp Chapel, The Collegiate Church of St. Mary, Warwick (Lisa Ford).
5. Tomb of William Bourchier, third Earl of Bath, and his wife, Elizabeth Russell. The Church of St. Peter, Tawstock, Devon (Lisa Ford).
6. Inscription stone from the tomb of Henry Howard, Earl of Surrey. The Church of St. Michael, Framlingham, Suffolk (Lisa Ford).
7. Inscription stone from the tomb of Henry Howard, Earl of Northampton. Trinity Hospital Greenwich, London (Lisa Ford).
8. Inscription stone from the tomb of Henry Howard, Earl of Surrey. The Church of St. Michael, Framlingham, Suffolk (Lisa Ford).

9. Photo taken during restoration of Surrey tomb at The Church of St. Michael, Framlingham, c. 1976. Archive of The Church of St. Michael, Framlingham.
10. Coronet presently on tomb of Henry Howard, Earl of Surrey, The Church of St. Michael, Framlingham, Suffolk (Lisa Ford).
11. Joshua Kirby, 'The Tomb of Henry Howard Earl of Surry', 1748, Joseph Wood, engraver. Archive of The Church of St. Michael, Framlingham.
12. Photo of Surrey tomb, The Church of St. Michael, Framlingham, Suffolk, with coronet near head of effigy, from J. Charles Cox, *English Church Fittings, Furniture & Accessories* (London 1923), 62.
13. Holes in cushion supporting head of Surrey's effigy on Surrey tomb, The Church of St. Michael, Framlingham, Suffolk (Lisa Ford).
14. Photo of Surrey tomb, c. 1976/7, during restoration, The Church of St. Michael, Framlingham, Suffolk, with the old coronet resting next to the handbrush by the effigy's head. Archive of The Church of St. Michael, Framlingham.
15. Photo of Surrey tomb, c. 1976/7, immediately after restoration, The Church of St. Michael, Framlingham, Suffolk, without coronet. Archive of The Church of St. Michael, Framlingham.
16. Photo of the old coronet removed from the Surrey tomb during restoration. Archive of The Church of St. Michael, Framlingham (Lisa Ford).
17. Photo from service of reconsecration of Surrey tomb, 9 July, 1977 at The Church of St. Michael, Framlingham, Suffolk. Archive of The Church of St. Michael, Framlingham.
18. Tomb of Thomas Coventry, 1st Earl of Coventry. Church of St. Mary, Elmley Castle, Worcester. Photo courtesy of Church Monuments Society.
19. Tomb of Henry Howard, Earl of Surrey and his wife, c. 1638, from Henry Lilly MS, G 1/16, f. 128, Arundel Castle Archives. By kind permission of His Grace the Duke of Norfolk.

INDEX

The index is strictly confined to the names of people and places, but it aims to be comprehensive. It does not, however, include the material in the footnotes or the captions to the illustrations.

INDEX